THE SCOTTISH SPORTS QUIZ BOOK

MARTIN GREIG

WAVERLEY
BOOKS

ACKNOWLEDGEMENTS

The author would like to thank all of the following people (in alphabetical order): Bill Abraham, Graeme Broadley, Allan Brown, Jason Cranwell, Jim Divers, Doug Gillon, Barry Graham, Andy Harbison, Kenny Hodgart, Douglas Lowe, Hugh 'the Mamba' MacDonald, Charlie McGarry, Graeme Macpherson, Jim O'Donnell, Mark Palmer, Alan Pattullo, Graeme Phanco, David Toner, Ed Watson and Richard Winton. Special thanks to George Greig and Martin 'Statto' Sutton.

Published 2010 by Waverley Books,
144 Port Dundas Road, Glasgow, G4 0HZ

A catalogue entry for this book is available from the British Library

ISBN 978-1-84934-024-3

Printed and bound in the UK

Contents

Foreword

There is an apocryphal tale of a philosophy undergraduate who enters his final exam and is confronted with the teaser: 'Is this a question?' After a few moments of deliberation, he writes: 'Is this an answer?' And promptly earns full marks. Readers of this book will not be asked to ponder any such deep philosophical issues, but it would help to know about Scottish sport in all its forms.

Football is Scotland's national sport and half of the book is given over to questions on it. Be prepared to tackle a wide-range of subjects including the Old Firm, Hearts and Hibs, the Scottish National Team, the Dundee Clubs and a substantial section on Junior Football.

Non-football afficionados will have a field day with the other half of the book. Enthusiasts of sports such as rugby, golf, cricket, boxing and motor sport are well catered for but there are posers on everything else from swimming, ice-skating and haggis-hurling to elephant polo.

The questions have three difficulty levels: the Premier Division questions are aimed at the real sporting know-it-alls while those with moderate knowledge should flick to the First Division ones; and others with limited knowledge will be able to have a stab at the easier Second Division questions. Within each Division there can be up to five pages of questions.

Good luck!

QUESTIONS

Celtic: Premier Division 1

1. Which two clubs did Jock Stein manage before taking charge of Celtic in March 1965?
2. Who was Jock Stein's last signing for Celtic, in 1978?
3. How many goals did Joe McBride score in season 1966–67 before sustaining the knee injury in December that would keep him out for half the season?
4. Joe McBride never scored against Rangers. True or false?
5. Who scored the winner for Celtic in the 1965 Scottish Cup final?
6. Who were Celtic's opposition in the 1965 Scottish Cup final?
7. Name the only three managers in Celtic's history to have won three consecutive league titles.
8. Who scored Celtic's third goal in their famous 6–2 victory over Rangers in August 2000?
9. From which club did Celtic sign Lubomir Moravcik in October 1998?
10. What was significant about the 1955 Scottish Cup final between Celtic and Clyde?
11. Which Lisbon Lion played in the 1980 Scottish Cup final against Rangers?
12. What Celtic player was awarded the Victoria Cross for valour on the Western Front in 1915?
13. Who played in goal for Celtic when they beat Rangers 5–1 at Celtic Park in November 1998?
14. Which defender, signed on a loan deal from Southampton, made his one and only appearance for Celtic in the 3–0 defeat by Rangers at Celtic Park in May 1999?
15. In the 1988 Scottish Cup final, who provided the cross for Frank McAvennie to equalize for Celtic after Dundee United had gone ahead?
16. Name the only Celtic player to miss a penalty in the incredible 11–10 CIS Insurance Cup semi–final penalty shoot–out victory over Dundee United in January 2009
17. Why was Celtic legend Billy McNeill nicknamed 'Cesar'?
18. What was the nickname of Bobby Lennox, the Lisbon Lion?
19. Who said: 'Celtic have all the cool people supporting them. Rangers have me and "Wet, Wet, Wet"'?
20. Who did Celtic beat in the final of the Coronation Cup in 1953?

Answers on page 163

Celtic: Premier Division 2

1. Who succeeded Billy McNeill as Celtic manager in 1983?
2. Against which club did Celtic legend Henrik Larsson score his 100th league goal on 6 April 2002?
3. Which former Aberdeen and St Mirren midfielder scored the winning goal in the first Old Firm game after Billy McNeill returned as Celtic manager in 1987?
4. What was the score in Celtic's first-ever game, against Rangers in 1888?
5. Who did Celtic face in Billy McNeill's testimonial match in 1974?
6. Which Lisbon Lion appeared for Birmingham in the Inter-Cities Fairs Cup final against Roma in 1961, a game the English club lost 4–2 on aggregate?
7. The Celtic View was the brainchild of which former Celtic chairman?
8. How many goals did Tom Boyd score in a Celtic career spanning 11 years and over 300 appearances – 1, 2, or 9?
9. Who did Celtic beat in the final of the Glasgow Cup in 1967?
10. Name two former Celtic strikers who played for Aston Villa before coming to Parkhead
11. In April 2006, John Hartson, on his 31st birthday, scored the only goal as Celtic clinched the championship with a narrow 1–0 victory at Celtic Park. Who did they beat?
12. Name the four Celtic players to have made their debuts in Old Firm games since 2001.
13. The fastest recorded goal in an Old Firm match was scored at Ibrox on 7 December 2002. Which Celtic striker gave his side the early advantage?
14. Andrew Kerins is better known by what title?
15. Excluding friendlies, how many matches in total did the Lisbon Lions start together – 1, 9 or 11?
16. Which former Hibs midfielder was Celtic's top goal scorer in season 1993–94?
17. Who was the first black player to play for Celtic?
18. Which Venezuelan international joined Celtic in 2000, his only start for the first team coming in a friendly against Bayern Munich?
19. How many times have Celtic won the domestic Treble?
20. Who was the second Celtic player Martin O'Neill signed from Leicester City?

Answers on page 163

Celtic: Premier Division 3

1. Celtic's record 11–0 win came against which team in season 1895–96?
2. In what year did Celtic adopt the famous hooped jersey?
3. Which early Celtic player was nicknamed 'the Icicle'?
4. The first Celtic crest had a green cross on it, but what colour was the background?
5. What caused Radio 5 Live to momentarily go off the air during a Celtic–Aberdeen game in 1996?
6. Who was sold to Blackpool for a record fee of £10,000 in 1937 less than three months after he had scored the winning goal in that year's Scottish Cup final for Celtic?
7. How many goals did Maurice Johnston score in his 127 games for Celtic – 65, 69 or 71?
8. Who scored eight goals for Celtic in a 9–1 win over Dunfermline in January 1928?
9. How many competitive appearances did Willo Flood make for Celtic – 5, 10 or 20?
10. Who were Celtic's scorers in the famous 5–0 victory over St Mirren at Love Street in 1986, which snatched the championship away from Hearts?
11. Which Celtic player was killed in a tragic accident when electrocuted at his home in Kilmarnock in 1981?
12. From which Welsh club did Celtic sign Jock Stein as a player?
13. Name the two Guinean internationals to have played for Celtic.
14. Which defender joined Celtic on loan from Sunderland in 2003?
15. Which Hungarian club did former Celtic reserve coach Willie McStay join as manager in 2009?
16. Which striker joined Celtic from Barnsley in 1993 but failed to score any goals in a forgettable four-month spell?
17. Which Celtic midfielder signed from Arsenal for £625,000 in May 1990 but failed to live up to expectations?
18. Which Celtic midfielder did Liam Brady sign for £1.5 million from West Ham in 1992?
19. Against which opposition did Marc-Antoine Fortune score his first 2 goals for Celtic in August 2009?
20. Which Celtic team-mate was Shunsuke Nakamura referring to when he said: 'I think he is a genius'?

Answers on page 164

Celtic: First Division 1

1. Who is Celtic's all-time leading goal scorer?
2. Who is Celtic's second all-time leading goal scorer?
3. Who did Roy Keane famously make his debut against in January 2006 and what was the score?
4. Which defender made his one and only appearance in a Celtic shirt the same day as Roy Keane's debut?
5. And who replaced him at halftime?
6. What was the name of Inter Milan's coach when Celtic faced the Italian giants in the European Cup final of 1967?
7. What nationality was he?
8. Name the 2 Brazilian internationals who have played for Celtic.
9. Who were the infamous 'Three Amigos' referred to by Celtic owner Fergus McCann?
10. What age was Celtic keeper John Thomson when he tragically died in a collision with Rangers striker Sam English in September 1931?
11. Who was Martin O'Neill's first signing as Celtic manager?
12. What was the nickname of former Celtic striker Charlie Nicholas?
13. What career did Lisbon Lion Jim Craig enter after retiring from football?
14. Who did Celtic beat to clinch the league in season 1997–98 and stop Rangers' march to 10-in-a-row?
15. Who said: 'What these players have to realize, is that when you put on the Celtic jersey you're not playing for a football team, you're playing for a community and a cause'?
16. Which member of the Feyenoord team that beat Celtic in the 1970 European Cup final went on to manage the Parkhead club?
17. Which Celtic player scored four goals in the 5–4 defeat of Partizan Belgrade in 1989?
18. Which Celtic player was described as the Scottish Roberto Baggio by Billy McNeill when breaking through in the late 1980s?
19. Who handed over the Scottish Cup to winning Celtic captain Roy Aitken in 1988?
20. Who did Celtic face in the Intercontinental Cup in 1968?

Answers on page164

Celtic: First Division 2

1. What was the name of Celtic's controversial general manager who was appointed in June 1997 and left in November the following year?
2. What tune was played over the PA system at Celtic Park whenever Henrik Larsson scored a goal?
3. Who said: 'If I'd had (Bobby) Lennox in my team I could have played forever. He was one of the best strikers I have ever seen'?
4. From which club did Celtic sign Brian McClair in 1983?
5. Which future Celtic defender played against the Parkhead club for Stuttgart in the 2003 UEFA Cup?
6. On New Year's Day 2006 Celtic came from 2–0 down at Tynecastle to win 3–2. Who scored a double in the last 5 minutes to complete a memorable comeback?
7. Name the Italian who returned to Celtic Park in December 2007 to take part in Phil O'Donnell's benefit game.
8. Against which French club did Celtic legend Henrik Larsson sustain his double leg fracture in 1999?
9. In injured Henrik Larsson's absence, who finished Celtic's top scorer in season 1999–2000?
10. Which Celtic goalkeeper holds the club record for clean sheets?
11. Which football icon who played for Real Madrid was so impressed by Jimmy Johnstone that he insisted Celtic were the team he wanted for his testimonial in 1967?
12. From which club did Celtic sign Andy Walker from?
13. Who was the SFA supremo who lost his job over failing to complete Jorge Cadete's registration in time?
14. Who was Celtic's physio during the 1980s and 90s?
15. Celtic were founded in which Glasgow Church?
16. Which Celtic player scored direct from a corner-kick away to Falkirk in the Scottish Cup in 1953 and, when ordered to retake it, scored again to help Celtic to a 3–2 victory?
17. Which former Celtic manager went on to win the League Cup with Livingston in 2003–04?
18. What theme tune was played whenever John Hartson scored a goal at Celtic Park?
19. Who was Jozef Venglos' assistant manager at Celtic?
20. Which brothers became the first and only siblings to score in the same Old Firm match for Celtic in a 3–0 victory on 2 April 1984?

Celtic: First Division 3

1. How many goals did Henrik Larsson score for Celtic?
2. Celtic's highest margin of victory in the SPL is 7 goals. One of these occasions came in an 8–1 defeat of Dunfermline at East End Park in February 2006. Who scored one of his only 3 goals in a 7-year spell at Parkhead that day?
3. What age was George Connelly when he retired from football?
4. What is the official capacity of Celtic Park to the nearest thousand?
5. What was the name of the DVD Celtic released after defeating Rangers 6–2 in August 2000?
6. In the 2007 Scottish Cup final, which Celtic defender scored his first senior goal in a 1–0 win?
7. What nationality is he?
8. How many Scotland caps did Jimmy Johnstone win?
9. Shunsuke Nakamura was Celtic's first Japanese signing. Who was their second?
10. Who was Gordon Strachan's assistant manager at Celtic?
11. What was the name of the stadium in which Celtic won the European Cup in 1967?
12. Javier Sanchez Broto and David Fernandez both joined Celtic from which Scottish club?
13. Since 1999, name 2 Celtic shirt sponsors
14. Which Celtic manager signed Lubo Moravcik?
15. Who was assistant to Wim Jansen in the 1997–98 season when Celtic ended Rangers' 10-in-a-row bid?
16. In Celtic's treble-winning 2000–2001 season, how many goals did Henrik Larsson score in the 3–0 CIS Insurance Cup final victory over Kilmarnock?
17. Who is the only player to have scored for Celtic in 2 European finals?
18. Who scored the goal that won the league for Celtic on the last day of the 2007–08 season against Dundee United at Tannadice?
19. Who was the Dundee United goalkeeper when Celtic clinched the 2007–08 SPL title at Tannadice who would sign for the Parkhead club the following year?
20. Celtic clinched 2 other loan deals on the same day Robbie Keane arrived from Spurs in January 2010. Name them.

Answers on page165

Celtic: Second Division 1

1. Which Celtic player did Gordon Strachan claim was technically the most accomplished performer he had ever played with or managed?
2. Who was voted Celtic's greatest-ever player by fans in 2002?
3. Who was the Scottish-born Canadian businessman who saved Celtic from the brink of bankruptcy in 1994?
4. Who scored the winning goal for Celtic against Inter Milan in the 1967 European Cup final?
5. Who was Celtic manager when the club won the Scottish Cup in 1995?
6. Who did Celtic beat in the 1995 Scottish Cup final?
7. Who scored the winning goal for Celtic in the 1995 Scottish Cup final?
8. What was the name of the Irish Marist brother who founded Celtic in 1888?
9. What is Celtic's nickname?
10. What is the name of the Celtic club mascot?
11. Who started Celtic's pre-match Huddle?
12. What is Celtic keeper Artur Boruc's nickname?
13. What street is Celtic Park on?
14. From which club did Celtic sign Paul Lambert from?
15. Who was Jock Stein's long-serving assistant at Celtic?
16. Name the 2 men who arrived as Celtic's supposedly management 'dream team' in 1999?
17. Which First-Division side beat Celtic in the Scottish Cup in February 2000, a result which led to the manager being sacked?
18. What was the famous headline in *The Sun* the next day?
19. Who was the Blackburn Rovers manager when Celtic overcame the English side en route to the 2003 UEFA Cup final?
20. What was the colloquial name for the standing enclosure at Celtic Park where the North Stand is now situated?

Celtic: Second Division 2

1. What is the name of the draw that is made at half-time at every match at Celtic Park?
2. Who was the Celtic chairman between 2000 and 2007?
3. Who succeeded Jock Stein as Celtic manager in 1978?
4. From which Italian club did Shunsuke Nakamura sign to Celtic in August 2005?
5. What number of shirt does Celtic's Aiden McGeady wear?
6. What was the name of Celtic's training ground that was used by the first team up until 2007?
7. Which former Celtic midfielder was nicknamed 'the Maestro'?
8. What is the name of the song sung by Celtic fans when they raise their scarves in the air?
9. What nationality is former Celtic striker Jorge Cadete?
10. Martin O'Neill won the domestic Treble in his first season in charge at Celtic. What trophies make up the Treble?
11. What is the name given to the derby match between Celtic and arch-rivals Rangers?
12. Who was the Celtic chairman during season 2009–10?
13. Who was the Celtic chairman at the time of the club's European Cup win in 1967?
14. Who said to Jock Stein in the aftermath of Celtic's European triumph in Lisbon in 1967: 'John, you're immortal'?
15. Who was Celtic captain from 1977 until 1987?
16. Who said: 'Celtic jerseys are not for second best. They don't shrink to fit inferior players'?
17. Name the Celtic chief executive during season 2009–10
18. What nationality is former Celtic manager Martin O'Neill?
19. Which club did Scott McDonald move to from Celtic in January 2010?
20. Which midfielder did Celtic pay Hibs £4.4million for in 2007?

Answers on page 166

Rangers: Premier Division 1

1. Which member of Rangers' famous 9-in-a-row team said: 'I only drink when I win a trophy. That's why people think I'm an alcoholic'?
2. In which country was former Rangers captain Richard Gough born?
3. How many Scotland caps did John Greig win – 34, 44 or 54?
4. From which club did Rangers sign Andrei Kanchelskis in 1998?
5. And how much was the fee?
6. Who was Rangers' first £1million signing?
7. How many trophies did John Greig win as Rangers manager?
8. What is Sandy Jardine's real first name?
9. Sandy Jardine played for Rangers from 1965 to 1982. How many managers did he play under – 3, 4 or 5?
10. Name 6 Dutch players who have played for Rangers.
11. Who has scored the most goals for Rangers in a single season?
12. How many did he score?
13. What was the name of Rangers' first manager?
14. Where did the name 'Rangers' come from?
15. How many trophies did Rangers win in the 1948–49 season?
16. What made the achievement even more significant?
17. Which former Rangers manager became the first man to play both football and cricket for Scotland?
18. Which Rangers player from the modern era played both football and cricket for Scotland?
19. How many goals did Brian Laudrup score for Rangers – 25, 35 or 45?
20. In which country was Brian Laudrup born?

Answers on page 167

Rangers: Premier Division 2

1. How many goals did Mark Hateley score for Rangers – 105, 115 or 120?
2. How many trophies did Mark Hateley win at Rangers?
3. What was Mark Hateley's nickname?
4. Which club signed Mark Walters from Rangers?
5. And which manager signed him for the Anfield club?
6. What age was Paul Gascoigne when he signed for Rangers?
7. How much did Rangers pay for Paul Gascoigne in July 1994?
8. How many appearances did Paul Gascoigne make for Rangers – 93, 103 or 113?
9. How many England caps did Paul Gascoigne win while at Rangers – 17, 22 or 27?
10. Who did Paul Gascoigne sign for when he left Rangers in March 1998?
11. In what year did Ian Durrant make his Rangers debut?
12. How many hat-tricks did Ally McCoist score for Rangers?
13. What was the highest number of hat-tricks Ally McCoist achieved in one season?
14. What was Ally McCoist's nickname during the Graeme Souness era at Rangers, when the striker often found himself on the bench?
15. Name the three players who featured in all of Rangers' 9-in-a-row titles.
16. Who is Rangers' third top post-war goal scorer behind Ally McCoist and Derek Johnstone?
17. Which Rangers player uniquely played for Scotland in defence, midfield and attack?
18. Which Rangers manager, after he left the club, went on to win the League Cup with Dundee in 1973–74?
19. Which Rangers winger from the 1920s and 30s was known by the nickname 'the Wee Blue Devil'?
20. Which two Scottish clubs did Rangers keeper Allan McGregor join for loan spells?

Answers on page 167

Rangers: Premier Division 3

1. Name the Italian striker who signed for Rangers on the last day of the transfer window at the start of the 2005–06 season but never played a game.
2. From whom did Sir David Murray buy Rangers in 1988?
3. Egil Ostenstad never scored a goal for Rangers. True or false?
4. Which Ibrox player was sent off in the title-clinching match when Rangers beat Celtic 3–0 at Parkhead in May 1999?
5. How many years did Bill Struth manage Rangers?
6. How many league titles did Bill Struth win as Rangers manager – 18, 19 or 20?
7. Who did Rangers pay a Scottish record fee for in 1960?
8. How much did they pay?
9. Name the only two Rangers managers not to win a major trophy.
10. Which player, who would go on to become a club legend, made his debut against Hearts in February 1967 at the age of 18, the week after Rangers' shock cup exit to Berwick Rangers?
11. What age was Derek Johnstone when he made his debut for Rangers?
12. How many caps did Derek Johnstone win for Scotland?
13. Graeme Souness was sent off on his debut for Rangers in the opening league game of the 1986 season. Who were the opposition that day?
14. Rangers broke the Scottish transfer record in 1968. Who did they sign?
15. What was the fee and why was it so significant?
16. Against which First Division side in the CIS Cup did Danny Wilson make his Rangers debut in October 2009?
17. Name the Rangers player who was the greatest-ever penalty taker in Scottish football.
18. Who was the unlikely scorer when Rangers beat Celtic 1–0 at Parkhead in March 2007?
19. Fernando Ricksen was substituted after 22 minutes of Rangers' 6–2 defeat by Celtic in August 2000. Who replaced him?
20. Name the French defender who scored on his Rangers debut against Livingston in July 2005, but quickly fell out of favour.

Answers on page 168

Rangers: First Division 1

1. Which Scottish club did Sir David Murray attempt to buy before taking over Rangers?
2. How many trophies did Alex McLeish win as Rangers manager?
3. Who was Rangers' shirt sponsor from 1987–99?
4. Which legendary former Rangers manager said: 'To be a Ranger is to sense the sacred trust of upholding all that the name means in this shrine of football ... No true Ranger has ever failed the tradition'?
5. Which club did Jim Baxter move to after leaving Rangers in 1965?
6. Which side upset the odds to beat Rangers in the Scottish Cup in 1987?
7. Who scored twice for Rangers in the league decider against Aberdeen in May 1991?
8. Name the rookie Aberdeen goalkeeper who was flattened early in that game by Rangers' scorer.
9. How many league titles in Rangers' 9-in-row run did Walter Smith win as manager?
10. How many times did Ally McCoist win the European Golden Boot?
11. Who did Ally McCoist sign for after finally ending his 15-year Rangers career in 1998?
12. Name the Rangers chairman who lured Graeme Souness to the role of player-manager from Sampdoria in April 1986.
13. From which club did England goalkeeper Chris Woods sign for Rangers?
14. Who was the first man to have been Rangers manager twice?
15. Who was the second man to have been Rangers manager twice?
16. Who was Walter Smith's first signing as Rangers manager?
17. How many trophies did Walter Smith win in his first full season as Rangers manager?
18. Who did Dick Advocaat manage before Rangers?
19. Who was Dick Advocaat's first signing for Rangers?
20. Name the two South Africans who have played for Rangers.

Answers on page 168

Rangers: First Division 2

1. Which English club did Bob Malcolm join after leaving Rangers in 2006?
2. Against whom did Alex McLeish win his first trophy, the CIS Cup, in March 2002?
3. What was the score?
4. Name the former Argentinean international who scored twice in that final.
5. Who were the opposition in Ally McCoist's last-ever game for Rangers?
6. Who was the first Rangers manager to be sacked?
7. What was unusual about the sacking?
8. How many goals did Ally McCoist score in Old Firm games – 23, 25 or 27?
9. What position did Rangers finish in the league in season 2005–06?
10. Who were the opposition in John Greig's testimonial in 1978?
11. Who were Rangers' closest challengers during the 9-in-a-row years between 1988–89 and 1996–97?
12. Rangers did not record a victory in the first three Old Firm games of Dick Adovcaat's stewardship. True or false?
13. How many days did Paul Le Guen's reign at Rangers last – 194, 198 or 202?
14. What was the name of the Slovakian striker who came to symbolize the mediocrity of Paul Le Guen's spell as Rangers manager?
15. What was the name of Dick Advocaat's assistant manager at Rangers?
16. From which club did Rangers sign Trevor Steven in 1989?
17. Which club did Trevor Steven move to from Rangers in 1991?
18. Who was the opposition in Rangers legend Davie Cooper's testimonial in 1988?
19. Who scored the late winner for Rangers in the penultimate Old Firm game of the 2009–10 season, which put the Ibrox club 10 points clear at the top of the league?
20. What was former Rangers goalkeeper Peter McCloy's nickname?

Answers on page 169

Rangers: First Division 3

1. Which manager brought Sasa Papac to Rangers?
2. What nationality is Rangers' Sasa Papac?
3. Against which side did John Fleck score his first goal for Rangers from the penalty spot in January 2009?
4. Name John Fleck's uncle who played for Rangers in the 1980s.
5. How many trophies did Dick Advocaat win in his first season at Rangers?
6. How many trophies did Dick Advocaat win in total during his spell at Rangers?
7. Which Rangers manager signed Davie Cooper from Clydebank in the summer of 1977?
8. What are the official names of Rangers' four stands?
9. Against which team did Kris Boyd break Henrik's Larsson 158–goal Scottish Premier League record in January 2009?
10. How many goals did Boyd score in the game?
11. Which Alfie was the first post-war player to play for Celtic and Rangers?
12. Who was the Romanian international defender who signed for Rangers and never played a game?
13. From which club did Rangers sign Mark Hateley in 1990?
14. Who was Alex McLeish's assistant at Rangers?
15. Name the Danish goalkeeper signed by Dick Advocaat for £2million in 2000 but who only played a handful of games?
16. Which former Rangers player was nicknamed 'Jukebox'?
17. Name the long-serving Rangers kitman.
18. TV chef Gordon Ramsay was once on Rangers' books. True or false?
19. What was former Rangers defender Dave McPherson's nickname?
20. How many goals did Francis Jeffers score for Rangers?

Answers on page 169

Rangers: Second Division 1

1. What is the Rangers club motto?
2. What was the name of Rangers' first home and where was it?
3. How many Rangers appearances did record holder John Greig make – 755, 785 or 804?
4. Which then England captain signed for Rangers in 1986?
5. Who was voted the greatest-ever Ranger by fans in 1999?
6. What nationality is former Rangers manager Paul Le Guen?
7. Which side did Paul Le Guen manage before taking the Rangers job?
8. Which club did Barry Ferguson sign for when he left Rangers in 2003?
9. Who did Barry Ferguson join when he left Rangers for a second time in 2009?
10. Which former Rangers manager signed Barry Ferguson in 2009?
11. What was former Rangers manager Dick Advocaat's nickname?
12. Who is Rangers' record signing?
13. And how much did the club pay for him?
14. What was legendary Rangers midfielder Jim Baxter's nickname?
15. What is the name of Rangers' state-of-the-art training facility on the outskirts of Glasgow?
16. In what year was it opened?
17. What is the colloquial name given to the final day of the 2004–05 season when Rangers stole the title from Celtic?
18. Who did Rangers beat the final day of the 2004–05 season?
19. Who scored their only goal?
20. With whom did Mark Hateley form a memorable striker partnership during his spell at Ibrox?

Rangers: Second Division 2

1. What was former Rangers keeper Andy Goram's nickname?
2. What height is former Rangers keeper Andy Goram?
3. Who did Rangers beat 6–1 to clinch the league on the final day of the 2002–03 season?
4. Who scored Rangers' 6th goal from the penalty spot that day?
5. In which year was the Ibrox disaster?
6. On which street is Ibrox Stadium?
7. Who did Giovanni van Bronckhorst sign for after leaving Rangers in 2001?
8. Which legendary Rangers keeper won the Champions League with Borussia Dortmund in 1997?
9. What nationality is former Rangers striker Peter Lovenkrands?
10. Which striker signed for Rangers in 2008 after previous spells at Derby County and Celtic?
11. From which Scottish club did Rangers sign Nacho Novo in 2004?
12. Who did Rangers sell Alan Hutton to in January 2008?
13. What was the fee?
14. Rangers lost the first Old Firm game of the 2000–01 season 6–2 to Celtic. However, they gained revenge in the second Old Firm game of the season. What was the score?
15. Which Norwegian international made his debut and scored the second goal in that game?
16. Which player controversially signed for Rangers in 1989 after earlier agreeing to join Celtic?
17. Who was the Rangers chairman during season 2009–10?
18. Who was Rangers chairman for over 20 years before finally stepping down in 2009?
19. Which former Rangers midfielder was nicknamed 'the Hammer'?
20. Which former Celtic reserve coach is now Rangers' first-team coach?

Answers on page170

Scottish National Team: Premier Division 1

1. How many times in total have Scotland reached the World Cup finals – 7, 8 or 9 times?
2. Why were Scotland ineligible to compete in the World Cups of 1930, 34 and 38?
3. Who was Scotland's first-ever manager?
4. Why did he resign before the second game of the 1954 Switzerland World Cup against Uruguay?
5. Scotland's trainer took charge of team affairs. What was his name?
6. What was the result of the match against Uruguay?
7. Who did Scotland lose to in their first game at the 1954 World Cup finals?
8. Which Hibs player appeared in both of Scotland's games at the 1954 Switzerland World Cup and later managed Scotland at the World Cup finals, becoming the only man to do so?
9. Who was meant to be Scotland manager at the 1958 World Cup in Sweden but could not fulfil his duties?
10. What was the reason?
11. Which legendary French striker scored his country's second goal in their 2–1 win over Scotland in the third group game at the 1958 World Cup?
12. He went on to set a World Cup scoring record which still stands. How many did he score?
13. Out of his 32 games in charge of Scotland, how many did Berti Vogts win – 7, 8 or 9?
14. How many new caps did Berti Vogts hand out as Scotland manager?
15. Which country did Berti Vogts go on to manage after Scotland?
16. What was the result in former Scotland manager Berti Vogts' final game against Moldova, a World Cup qualifier in October 2004?
17. Who scored for Scotland in that game?
18. The late Tommy Burns took charge for one match following Berti Vogts' departure. Who was Scotland's opposition for that friendly in November 2004?
19. And what was the score?
20. Name the former Aston Villa striker who scored twice for Scotland's opponents.

Answers on page 171

Scottish National Team: Premier Division 2

1. Scotland have qualified for the World Cup finals 6 times since 1974. Name the 5 managers who led them to qualification.
2. Who were Scotland's opposition in their opening game at the Mexico 86 World Cup?
3. And what was the score?
4. Scotland scored just one goal at Mexico 86. Who scored it?
5. And who were the opposition?
6. Scotland recorded a famous victory over a Portugal team containing Eusebio in 1971. Who was the Scotland manager?
7. Who were the opposition when Kenny Dalglish made his Scotland debut in November 1971?
8. And which former Hibs and Arsenal player did he replace?
9. Which famous manager took temporary charge of Scotland for 2 games, both in the 1958 British Home Championship?
10. Who was the Scotland manager who led the team to their famous 3–2 win over World Cup holders England at Wembley in 1967?
11. Name the scorers in that famous 3–2 win.
12. Who captained Scotland to that famous victory?
13. Which player made his international debut that day at the age of 36?
14. How many caps did Gary McAllister win – 52, 57 or 63?
15. How many goals did Ally McCoist score for Scotland – 17, 19 or 21?
16. Name the friendly opponents in September 1987 when Ally McCoist scored his first 2 Scotland goals.
17. How many times did Ally McCoist captain Scotland?
18. How many caps did Nigel Quashie win for Scotland – 10, 12 or 14?
19. Nigel Quashie was born in England, so how did he qualify for Scotland?
20. Who is Scotland's 3rd-top goal scorer?

Answers on page 171

Scottish National Team: Premier Division 3

1. Who is Scotland's 4th-top goal scorer?
2. What is Scotland's biggest-ever winning margin?
3. What is Scotland's heaviest-ever defeat?
4. Which player has captained Scotland more than any other?
5. Name the player who was capped twice for Scotland while at Liverpool but did not represent them in a league game.
6. Name the Scottish winger who was sent off against Argentina in a friendly in Buenos Aires in June 1977.
7. Which former Hearts keeper made his international debut against West Germany in 1963–64 and won his last cap 12 years later?
8. Who was the first Scottish international to be sold for over £1million?
9. Which South African-born player won 19 Scottish caps during the 1950s and 60s?
10. Which former Scotland goalkeeper also played outfield for Aberdeen in the 1969–70 season?
11. How many Scotland caps did Sir Matt Busby win?
12. Which 11-times capped Scotland defender won the league with Dundee in 1962 and went on to play for Arsenal?
13. Which Dutchwoman was appointed Scotland women's national coach in 1994?
14. Who was the first woman to win 100 caps for Scotland?
15. Which legend appeared in his one-and-only World Cup game in the opening match against Zaire in 1974, winning his 50th and last Scotland cap?
16. Scotland beat Zaire 2–0 at World Cup 74. Who scored their goals?
17. Scotland failed to qualify for the 1970 World Cup. Who did they finish second to in their qualifying group?
18. During Scotland's unsuccessful qualifying campaign for the 1994 World Cup their home matches could not be staged at Hampden, which was under redevelopment. Name the two alternative venues.
19. What was the name of Scotland's official World Cup song in 1978?
20. Which famous singer featured on lead vocals?

Scottish National Team: Premier Division 4

1. What was the name of Scotland's official World Cup song in 1990?
2. Who was Scotland's kit manufacturer in 1978?
3. When Danny McGrain returned from the 1974 World Cup, what medical condition was he diagnosed with?
4. Tom Boyd only scored one goal for Scotland in 72 appearances. Who was it against?
5. Against whom did James McFadden score his first goal for Scotland?
6. Who saved a penalty for Scotland against Portugal in a 2–0 friendly defeat in November 2002?
7. Who missed the penalty for Portugal?
8. Who scored the winner when Scotland beat Iceland 2–1 at Hampden in 2003?
9. Which then Middlesbrough player made 5 appearances for Scotland in 2002?
10. Against whom did Craig Burley win his last Scotland cap?
11. Which Italian defender scored the stoppage-time winner to effectively end Scotland's hopes of qualifying for Euro 2008?
12. Who scored Italy's first goal in their 2–1 Euro 2008 qualifier victory at Hampden?
13. Who was the Italian manager in their 2–1 Euro 2008 qualifier victory at Hampden?
14. Who scored Scotland's late strike to overcome Georgia 2–1 at Hampden in the Euro 2008 qualifying campaign?
15. How many of his 20 Scotland caps did Ian Durrant win at Kilmarnock – 7, 9 or 11?
16. Which midfielder, when about to appear as a very late substitute for England under-21s, took ages to tie his boots and never entered the field of play, ensuring he was still eligible to play for Scotland?
17. Jim Bett's only goal in 26 appearances for Scotland gave them a crucial 1–0 victory over which opponents in May 1985?
18. Which club did he sign for days after that strike?
19. Against which friendly opposition did Scott Brown make his Scotland debut in November 2005?
20. Alan Hansen's older brother John was also a Scottish international. True or false?

Answers on page 172

Scottish National Team: Premier Division 5

1. How many caps did Alan Hansen win for Scotland – 26, 36 or 46?
2. Who did Scotland crucially lose 2–0 to in the Euro 2008 qualifying campaign, a result which made the task of qualifying extremely difficult?
3. Scotland wore a new strip that night. What colour was it?
4. Who managed Georgia to victory and also led Bayer Leverkusen to the Champions League final at Hampden in 2002?
5. Who topped Scotland's Euro 2000 qualifying group by winning all of the 10 games they played?
6. Scotland beat Sweden 1–0 at home in a World Cup 1998 qualifying match. Where did the game take place?
7. Who scored Scotland's winner that day?
8. Name three Swedes who played in their 1–0 1998 defeat in Scotland who have played for either Celtic or Rangers.
9. Who was Scotland's top scorer at the 1982 World Cup finals with 2 goals?
10. In which film does Pat Nevin appear on the television in the background scoring a goal for Scotland against the USA in a 1992 friendly match in Denver?
11. George Burley's reign as Scotland manager started with a 1–1 draw in a friendly in March 2008. Who were the opposition?
12. Who scored Scotland's goal that night?
13. Of his 14 matches in charge at Scotland, how many did George Burley win – 2, 3 or 4?
14. And name the teams they beat in those games.
15. How many goals did Duncan Ferguson score in his 7 Scotland appearances?
16. Duncan Ferguson's last Scotland cap was against Estonia in 1997 in a World Cup qualifier. What was the score?
17. Why was Scotland's away game against Estonia in 1997 played in Monaco?
18. How many caps did Scotland boss Craig Levein win as a player?
19. Name the Frenchman and former manager of Japan who was in the frame for the Scotland job before Berti Vogts' appointment?
20. The Czech Republic defeated Scotland 2–1 at Hampden Park in the Euro 2000 qualifying campaign. True or false?

Answers on page 173

Scotland National Team: First Division 1

1. In which year did Scotland play in the World Cup finals without losing a game?
2. Who was the manager?
3. Why did Scotland not progress?
4. What was the score against the Netherlands in Scotland's opening game of the European Championship finals in 1996?
5. In their second game of Euro 96, Scotland lost 2–0 to England. Who missed a penalty for Scotland that day?
6. Who scored England's first goal against Scotland at Euro 96?
7. Scotland ended Euro 96 on a high with a 1–0 win over Switzerland. Who scored their goal?
8. Who scored the Netherlands' consolation goal in a 4–1 defeat by England to ensure that Scotland exited Euro 96 on goal difference?
9. In 2002, who said: 'The sun is shining, the birds are singing and we have a new Scotland manager'?
10. Alex McLeish was in charge of Scotland for 10 matches. How many did he win – 5, 7 or 9?
11. Who did Scotland lose 3–1 to in the opening game of the 1978 World Cup finals in Argentina?
12. Which Scotland player missed a penalty in that game?
13. What was the score in Scotland's final group game against Holland in the 1978 World Cup?
14. Who scored twice in that game including arguably the most famous strike in Scotland history?
15. Who was Scotland's other scorer against the Dutch?
16. Who scored the crucial goal for Holland which eliminated Scotland?
17. Which Scotland winger was banned for life after failing a drug test at World Cup 78?
18. Who is the only Scottish player to have scored in 3 successive World Cup finals?
19. What was the name of Scotland's first official World Cup song in 1974?
20. What number did it reach in the charts?

Answers on page 173

Scotland National Team: First Division 2

1. Who is Scotland's second-highest cap holder?
2. And how many caps does he have?
3. How many times have Scotland qualified for the European Championships?
4. Where were the championships held?
5. The first-ever Scotland team was made up of players from which Scottish club?
6. Alex McLeish has been capped more times than Paul McStay. True or false?
7. Who did Scotland beat 5–2 in their opening group match at the 1982 World Cup finals?
8. Scotland lost 4–1 to Brazil in their second group game at the 1982 World Cup finals. Name two of Brazil's scorers.
9. Scotland failed to qualify after failing to beat the USSR in their final group game at the 1982 World Cup finals. What was the score?
10. Who did Scotland beat to qualify for the World Cup finals in Germany in 1974?
11. Jim Holton scored for Scotland that night but who struck the winner?
12. Name the brothers who represented Scotland in the 1970s and played together for a leading English club.
13. And which brother won more caps?
14. Which former Scotland international started his career at Spurs but never made an appearance for them?
15. In which year was the first-ever Scotland–England match?
16. Where was the first-ever Scotland–England match played?
17. What was the score?
18. What was the name given to the Scotland team who beat England 5–1 in 1928?
19. Which Scotland striker scored a hat-trick in the 5–1 defeat of England in 1928?
20. Scotland beat Sweden 2–1 in their second group game at Italia 90. Who scored the winning penalty?

Answers on page 174

Scotland National Team: First Division 3

1. Who did Scotland lose to in their last group game at World Cup 1990?
2. And who scored for their opponents that night?
3. Which former Scotland women's international was inducted into the Scottish Football Hall of Fame in 2007?
4. Who scored a penalty for Scotland against England at Wembley in 1981 to clinch a 1–0 victory?
5. Which Scotland international won the European Cup Winners' Cup with Spurs in 1963?
6. He died tragically the following year. How did he die?
7. 'Sing when you're whaling, you only sing when you're whaling.' What opposition fans was this Tartan Army chant directed at in the 1998 World Cup finals?
8. Who made 34 appearances for the Scotland under-21 team, a world record at that level?
9. Barry Ferguson has had an illustrious Scotland career, but his older brother Derek failed to win any caps. True or false?
10. Scotland drew 1–1 with Norway in their second match at France 98. Who scored for the Scots?
11. What was the score when Morocco beat Scotland in their final group game of France 98?
12. Which Scotland player was sent off against Morocco at France 98?
13. Scotland's squad at Italia 90 included two players from the German Bundesliga. Name them.
14. Name the three Scottish internationals to have played in Serie A.
15. Gary Naysmith has only scored one goal in his Scotland career. Who was it against?
16. Scotland fielded 5 debutants against Japan in a 0–0 draw in the Kirin Cup in 1995. Name two of them.
17. Who was the first black player to represent Scotland?
18. And where was he born?
19. Who was the second black player to have represented Scotland?
20. What was George Burley doing when he found out he had been named Scotland boss in 2008?

Answers on page 174

1.   Name the Celtic and Rangers players doing battle in a recent Old Firm clash.

Answers on page 240

2.   Who is this Celtic player from the 1970s?

Answers on page 240

© DC Thomson & Co. Ltd.

3. Henrik Larsson is pictured lifting the Scottish Cup with team-mate Jackie McNamara in May 2004 after Celtic beat Dunfermline 3-1. How many goals did the Swedish striker score in the final?

Answers on page 240

4. Name the four Rangers legends pictured at the 30th anniversary of Rangers winning the Cup Winners' Cup in 1972

© DC Thomson & Co. Ltd.

Answers on page 240

© DC Thomson & Co. Ltd.

5. Andy Goram is a legend at Rangers but he also joined Manchester United on a brief loan spell in the 2000-01 season. How many appearances did he make – 1, 2 or 3?

6. Who is this millionaire businessman who bought a majority shareholding in Hearts in 2005?

Answers on page 240

© DC Thomson & Co. Ltd.

7.   Who is this former Hearts captain?

Answers on page 240

8. Who is this Hibs player celebrating a goal?

Answers on page 240

Scotland National Team: First Division 4

1. Who was sent off in their last match for Scotland after elbowing a San Marino player in 2001?
2. Who scored in the 1–0 victory over Italy in a World Cup qualifier at Hampden Park in 1965?
3. Which Scottish international team-mate was Pat Crerand describing when he said: 'He didn't just dominate matches, he took them over. He was also a headbanger'?
4. 'Bremner may turn out to be the best player in the World Cup. He is an inspiration to his side.' Who was describing Billy Bremner after Scotland's 0–0 draw with Brazil at the 1974 World Cup?
5. Which Scotland team-mate was Archie Gemmill describing when he said: 'If he was a chocolate drop he would eat himself'?
6. Who said: 'On my first day as Scotland manager I had to call off training after half an hour because nobody could get the ball off Jimmy Johnstone'?
7. 'Cheats and cowards … the scum of world football.' Who described the Uruguay team in this way after Scotland's 0–0 draw in the 1986 World Cup finals?
8. Which French player, in the aftermath of their 1–0 defeat to Scotland in Paris in September 2007, said: 'Losing tonight was like being smashed on the back of the head and then robbed'?
9. Who was in goal for Wales when Scotland beat them 1–0 to qualify for the 1986 World Cup?
10. Who was Wales' strike partnership when Scotland beat them 1–0 to qualify for the 1986 World Cup?
11. Who did Scotland's penalty scorer Davie Cooper replace in the second half in the Wales match?
12. How many goals did Paul McStay score for Scotland – 5, 9 or 12?
13. Charlie Miller never won a Scotland cap. True or false?
14. How many caps did John Collins win – 48, 58 or 68?
15. Which rugby-playing area of Scotland did football star John Collins hail from?
16. John Collins won a French league championship medal with Monaco. True or false?
17. Jim Craig, the Lisbon Lion, never played for Scotland. True or false?
18. Scotland lost their first group game 1–0 to Holland at the 1992 European Championship finals in Sweden. Who scored for the Dutch?
19. After losing 2–0 in their second game to Germany, Scotland restored pride in their 3rd and final match at Euro 92 by beating the CIS 3–0. Name Scotland's three scorers.
20. Which Scotland goalkeeper played between the sticks for the Great Britain Olympic side of 1948?

Answers on page 175

Scotland National Team: First Division 5

1. In the first game at the 1996 European Championships in England, Scotland drew 0–0 with Holland. They beat Switzerland 1–0 at the same venue in their 3rd match. What stadium did they play at?
2. Which Scotland and Celtic defender was sent off for kicking an opponent on the backside against West Germany in 1969?
3. Who scored a debut goal for Scotland against the Czech Republic in a friendly in May 2008?
4. And what was the score?
5. Who did Scotland beat in a play-off to qualify for the Mexico 86 World Cup?
6. And what was the score?
7. Who was Scotland manager for the 1986 World Cup?
8. Who was the Scotland assistant manager for the 1986 World Cup?
9. Name the only Scotland manager to follow up qualification for a World Cup with qualification for a European Championship.
10. Jimmy Johnstone, Billy McNeill, Jim Baxter and John Greig never played for Scotland in a World Cup finals. True or false?
11. Who did Scotland manager Craig Levein appoint as his national team scout in January 2010?
12. 'I'm English but I just wanted to further my career and Scotland gave me that chance.' Which ex-England under-21 player said this when he joined the Scotland squad for the first time in 2007?
13. Richard Gough made the last of his 61 appearances for Scotland in 1993 in a heavy defeat by Portugal. What was the score in that game?
14. Which striker who would go on to play for Celtic scored that night?
15. What was the score when Scotland faced the Faroe Islands in Toftir in a European Championship qualifier in 2002?
16. Who scored twice for the Faroe Islands?
17. What was his main profession?
18. Name Scotland's second-half scorers against the Faroes.
19. Name the West Brom striker who started for Scotland against the Faroes.
20. Name three of Scotland's four group opponents for Euro 2012.

Answers on page 175

Scotland National Team: Second Division 1

1. Who did Scotland lose to on penalties in the final of the Under-16 World Championships at Hampden in 1989?
2. Who was the Scotland under-16 manager that day?
3. Scotland beat England 1–0 in the European Championship play-off second leg at Wembley in 1999. Who scored Scotland's only goal?
4. Who were Scotland's opponents in the opening match of the France 1998 World Cup?
5. Who scored Scotland's goal from the penalty spot in that game?
6. Who was unfortunate enough to score an own goal in that game?
7. In which stadium do Scotland play their home matches?
8. Who is Scotland's most-capped player?
9. And how many caps did he win?
10. Who famously declared that Scotland would come back with 'at least a medal' from the World Cup finals in Argentina in 1978?
11. Scotland earned a 1–1 draw at Ninian Park against Wales in September 1985 to qualify for the 1986 World Cup. What tragic event occurred that night?
12. What was the name given to the scandal involving Barry Ferguson and Allan McGregor, who indulged in a drinking session after Scotland's 3–0 defeat by Holland in March 2009?
13. Who are Scotland's joint-top goal scorers?
14. How many goals have they scored?
15. Which English pundit described David Narey's opening goal against Brazil in Scotland's second group game at the 1982 World Cup finals as a 'toepoke'?
16. Who did Scotland lose to in their opening match of the 1990 World Cup finals?
17. Who was Scotland manager at the 1990 World Cup?
18. Which legendary footballer scored his first goal for Argentina against Scotland in a friendly at Hampden Park in 1979?
19. Which former Wimbledon, Spurs and Chelsea keeper represented Scotland 28 times between 1997 and 2003?
20. Which Scotland international appeared alongside Pele and Sylvester Stallone in the movie *Escape to Victory*?

Answers on page 176

Scotland National Team: Second Division 2

1. What age was James McFadden when he made his Scotland debut in 2002?
2. Who were the opposition when James McFadden made his Scotland debut in 2002?
3. Who was the opposition in Walter Smith's first match in charge of Scotland in 2005?
4. What was the score?
5. Who was appointed SFA chief executive in June 2007?
6. Who did he succeed in that role?
7. Who was the chief executive of the SFA between 1990 and 1999?
8. What is the national anthem of the Scotland team?
9. And who described it as 'a bit of a dirge' in 2003?
10. Who sustained a career-ending injury while playing for Scotland against Romania in a friendly at Hampden on 31 March 2004?
11. Who was former Scotland manager Alex McLeish talking about when he said: 'He has got that gallusness that you associate with famous Scottish players of the past, that kind of swagger'?
12. Who said of his club and international team-mate Kenny Dalglish: 'I never saw anyone in this country to touch him. I can think of only two who could possibly go ahead of him – Pele and possibly Cryuff'?
13. Who scored for Scotland against France at Hampden Park in October 2006 to clinch a famous 1–0 victory?
14. And who took the corner that led to the goal?
15. Which lower-division club plays its fixtures at Hampden Park?
16. Who was the Scotland women's team's coach during season 2009–10?
17. What nationality is she?
18. What colour is Scotland's home kit?
19. What symbol is on Scotland's badge?
20. Who was the president of the SFA during season 2009–10?

Answers on page 176

Scotland National Team: Second Division 3

1. Who was the Scotland under-21 manager during season 2009–10?
2. Who did Berti Vogts appoint as under-21 manager when he was made Scotland boss in 2002?
3. Who was Berti Vogts' assistant manager at Scotland?
4. What nationality is former Scotland manager Berti Vogts?
5. Who were Walter Smith's two assistants when he was manager of Scotland?
6. What is the nearest train station to Hampden Park?
7. What was the colloquial name given to the noise made by a big crowd inside Hampden Park?
8. Hampden Park was named after an Englishman. True or false?
9. What is Scotland striker James McFadden's nickname?
10. Craig Brewster never won a Scotland cap. True or false?
11. What colour of hair did Billy Bremner have?
12. Which Scotland striker spent six weeks in Barlinnie prison in 1996 for headbutting an opponent while playing for Rangers?
13. What is the collective name given to the Scotland supporters?
14. What is the name of the song associated with Scotland which starts: 'Hark where the night is falling, Hark hear the pipes a calling ... '
15. Scotland lost to Italy in their final qualifying match for World Cup 2008. Who scored Scotland's only goal?
16. The 1982 World Cup song 'We have a Dream' featured which Scottish actor on vocals?
17. Finish this Tartan Army chant: 'Six foot two, eyes of blue ... '
18. What actual height was he?
19. Archie Gemmill's son played 26 times for Scotland. What is his name?
20. Which goalkeeper was omitted from Craig Levein's first Scotland squad?

Scotland National Team: Second Division 4

1. Finish the rest of this lyric: 'O Flower of Scotland ... '
2. Which famous song by The Proclaimers has become an anthem for The Tartan Army?
3. What is the name of the much smaller stadium located behind the western end of Hampden Park?
4. Which Scotland keeper conceded nine goals against England at Wembley in 1961?
5. Which Scotland midfielder famously played 'keepie uppie' during the 3–2 victory over England in 1967 at Wembley?
6. What woman is Scotland's all-time leading scorer?
7. Which two Scotland defenders infamously collided to allow the USSR to go 2–1 ahead at the 1982 World Cup?
8. Which Englishman did George Burley appoint as his assistant manager?
9. Who missed a sitter for Scotland against Norway in a World Cup qualifier in October 2008?
10. Which striker refused to play for Scotland again under George Burley after being left on the bench for the World Cup qualifier against Norway in October 2008?
11. Who was the Argentina manager when they played Scotland in a friendly match at Hampden in November 2008?
12. What was the score when Argentina played Scotland in a friendly match at Hampden in November 2008?
13. Scotland beat the Faroe Island 6–0 in a European Championship qualifier in September 2006. At which Scottish ground was the game played?
14. Name two of Scotland's four scorers when they beat the Faroe Island 6–0 in a European Championship qualifier in September 2006
15. Which brothers played in central defence for Scotland in the 4–0 loss to Norway in August 2009?
16. One of them was sent off in that game – which one?
17. Who had to be rescued by the coastguard after getting stranded at sea in a rowing boat at the Scotland squad's Largs retreat in 1974?
18. Which film featured Archie Gemmill's goal against Holland in the background to a sex scene?
19. What is the name of the tartan headgear, with ginger tufts of hair attached to it, worn by Scotland supporters?
20. Who captained Scotland on their famous night in Paris when they defeated the French 1–0 in September 2007?

Answers on page 177

Scotland National Team: Second Division 5

1. True or false – Berti Vogts was the first foreigner to be named Scotland manager?
2. Who inflicted Scotland's worst defeat in 42 years in the Euro 2004 play-off second leg?
3. What was the score?
4. Who scored a hat-trick for Scotland's conquerors that night?
5. Who was the last Scotland manager to lead the country to a major championship?
6. What was the last major championship Scotland qualified for?
7. In which country was that championship held?
8. What was the name of Andy Cameron's World Cup song for the 1978 finals which reached number six in the charts?
9. Which English team did Craig Burley play for when he picked up his first cap for Scotland?
10. Which English team did Craig Burley play for when he made his last Scotland appearance in 2003?
11. Why was Craig Levein's introductory press conference as Scotland manager delayed?
12. Who is Craig Levein's Scotland assistant?
13. Which team did Scotland beat in Craig Levein's first game in charge?
14. Who scored Scotland's only goal?
15. Who are Scotland's official kit supplier?
16. Who was the Scotland captain during season 2009–10?
17. Who was the previous Scotland skipper?
18. How many caps does a player need to win to be inducted into the SFA Hall of Fame?
19. Name the founding member of the Corries who sings the national anthem before games.
20. Name the Hearts and former England under-21 winger who thought he was eligible for Scotland only to discover that he had not attended school long enough in the country to qualify

Answers on page 178

Scottish Clubs in Europe: Premier Division 1

1. Name the Celtic player who scored the fastest-ever European club competition hat-trick in 2000.
2. Celtic's first-ever European match was in the Inter-Cities Fairs Cup in season 1962–63. Who did they play?
3. Name the Celt who struck twice in that tie to become the club's first scorer in a European match.
4. Celtic defeated MTK Budapest 3–0 in the Cup Winners' Cup first leg semi-final in 1963–64. What was the score in the second leg?
5. Who scored Celtic's goal in the 1970 European Cup semi-final first-leg 1–0 win against Leeds at Elland Road?
6. In December 2001 Celtic were denied a place in the 4th round of the UEFA Cup when they lost on penalties to Valencia. Name the Celtic player who missed two penalties in the shoot-out.
7. Who was the Valencia head coach when they defeated Celtic in the UEFA Cup on penalties in 2001?
8. In September 2001, which Juventus striker was awarded a dubious late penalty which he converted in the Italian side's 3–2 Champions League victory over Celtic?
9. Who was the Celtic defender who was adjudged to have fouled Amoruso?
10. In the Champions League group stage in 2006–07 Celtic won and lost to Benfica by the same scoreline. What was the result in both games?
11. Name Celtic's two scorers in the home victory over Benfica.
12. In the away game, which Celtic defender scored an own goal after 10 minutes?
13. Who scored Celtic's first goal in their 2–1 second-leg victory against Dinamo Moscow to help send them through to the final round of Champions League qualifying in 2009?
14. Celtic lost to Arsenal in a Champions League qualifier in 2009. What was the aggregate score?
15. Who did Rangers have a Battle of Britain clash with in 1961?
16. What was the score?
17. Name the two Rangers scorers over both legs.
18. Name two of the Sevilla scorers when they beat Rangers 4–1 in the Champions League in September 2009?
19. Rangers lost 4–1 to Unirea Urziceni in their Champions League campaign in October 2009. Who scored the Gers' only goal?
20. What country are Rangers' 2009 Champions League opponents Unirea Urziceni from?

Answers on page 178

Scottish Clubs in Europe: Premier Division 2

1. Who did Rangers beat in the semi–final of the Cup Winners' Cup in 1972?
2. What was the aggregate score?
3. Who scored Rangers first-ever European goal in 1956?
4. How many times did Rangers draw 0–0 in their UEFA Cup run in the 2007–08 season?
5. Who scored Rangers' winning penalty in the shoot-out against Fiorentina to take them to the 2008 UEFA Cup final in Manchester?
6. Name the 5 players who started every game for Rangers in their 2007–08 UEFA Cup campaign.
7. What was significant about the 1992–93 Champions League competition which Rangers competed in?
8. Name Rangers' 3 opponents in the group stage of the Champions League in season 1992–93.
9. What was the score in Rangers' opening group game of the 1992-93 Champions League against their French opponents?
10. Who scored Rangers' first goal that night?
11. Rangers beat Club Brugge 2–1 at Ibrox in the 1992–93 Champions League campaign. Which player did they have sent off against the Belgians?
12. Who did Ian Ferguson score against in Rangers' second group game in the 1992–93 Champions League to seal a 1–0 victory?
13. When Rangers beat Club Brugge 2–1 at Ibrox in March 1993 their winning goal came from an unlikely source. Who?
14. In season 2000–01, who were Rangers' three opponents in the Champions League group stage?
15. In August 1999, which Italian side did Rangers beat 2–0 in the first leg of the third qualifying round of the Champions League?
16. Who were their scorers that night?
17. Which Italian defender was sent off in that game?
18. Who scored the winner for Kaunas in the 2008 Champions League qualifier second leg to knock Rangers out?
19. Who scored Rangers' opening goal in the away leg of their Champions League qualifier against Kaunas in 2008?
20. Name 3 former Rangers players who have won the European Cup/Champions League.

Answers on page 179

Scottish Clubs in Europe: Premier Division 3

1. Name the only Scottish club to have won two European trophies and what trophies were they?
2. Who was the manager of Ferencvaros when they beat Hearts 1–0 in the UEFA Cup in December 2004?
3. Where was Hearts' 1–0 defeat to Ferencvaros in 2004 played?
4. Name the first Dundee United player to be capped by Scotland.
5. In which year did Dundee United reach the European Cup semi-final?
6. Who were their opponents?
7. Who managed Dunfermline when they defeated Valencia 6–2 in the second home leg of their Inter-Cities Fairs Cup tie in 1962?
8. What was the score in the away first leg of Dunfermline's Inter-Cities Fairs Cup tie against Valencia in 1962?
9. How did the victors eventually progress to the next round?
10. In the qualifying stages of the 1983 Cup Winners' Cup, who did Aberdeen beat 11–1 over two legs?
11. Who scored for Bayern Munich when Aberdeen beat the Germans 3–2 at Pittodrie in 1983?
12. Who knocked Aberdeen out at the semi-final stage of the Cup Winners' Cup in 1984?
13. Which former Aberdeen player became the first Scot to win the Intercontinental Cup?
14. And who did he win it with?
15. When was the last time Aberdeen played English opposition in a competitive match and what was the result?
16. Name Aberdeen's scorers in the 4–1 first-leg win in their UEFA Cup qualifying tie against Žalgiris Vilnius in 1996
17. What was the score in the second leg of Aberdeen's UEFA Cup qualifying tie against Žalgiris Vilnius in 1996?
18. What was the name of the team who knocked Aberdeen out of the UEFA Cup at the qualifying round stage in August 2000?
19. What was historically significant about that result?
20. Who was the Aberdeen manager at that point?

Answers on page 179

Scottish Clubs in Europe: Premier Division 4

1. How many goals did Alan Gilzean score in Dundee's run to the semi-final of the European Cup in season 1962–63?
2. Who was the manager of Dundee when they reached the semi-final of the European Cup in season 1962–63?
3. Who did the Dens Park club eventually lose to in the last four?
4. Which Scottish team produced the greatest recovery in a European match in September 1964?
5. Which former Dundee United and Motherwell manager played in that game?
6. Which Scottish team were the first British club to play in Europe?
7. What year was it?
8. How far did they get?
9. Name the Hibs player who scored 8 times for the club in European competitions.
10. In which year did Hibs last progress beyond the first round of European competition?
11. Who did they beat in the first round of the UEFA Cup?
12. Which goalkeeper was Hibs captain for that tie?
13. Which team knocked them out in the second round?
14. In 1974, who did Hibs trounce 12–3 on aggregate in the first round of the UEFA Cup?
15. Which Italian side beat Hibs 8–2 on aggregate in the second round of the UEFA Cup in 1974?
16. Which team did Queen of the South lose to in the second qualifying round of the UEFA Cup in August 2008?
17. What country were they from?
18. And which former Celtic midfielder was their manager?
19. Queens lost the home tie 2–1. Where was it played?
20. Who scored a spectacular free-kick in the second leg to give Queens hope?

Scottish Clubs in Europe: First Division 1

1. Who were Celtic's opposition in the first round of the UEFA Cup in 2002–03?
2. Which Blackburn Rovers player said, despite their 1–0 defeat in the first leg of the UEFA Cup second-round tie in 2002–03 against Celtic, that it had been 'boys against men – and we were the men'?
3. Celtic overcame Liverpool in the last eight of the 2002–03 UEFA Cup. Who scored the last goal of the second leg that sealed the tie for Celtic?
4. Who was manager of Liverpool when Celtic put them out of the UEFA Cup in 2003?
5. Which Celtic player missed a penalty in the semi-final first-leg 1–1 draw with Boavista at Celtic Park in March 2003?
6. Who captained Celtic in Seville at the 2003 UEFA Cup final?
7. Which Porto player played against Celtic at the UEFA Cup final in Seville in 2003 and then went on to play for Rangers?
8. Who scored the extra-time winner for Porto against Celtic in the 2003 UEFA Cup final?
9. Who knocked Celtic out of the quarter-final of the UEFA Cup in 2003–04?
10. Name the Argentinean midfielder who was the standout performer.
11. Which former Celtic striker scored a double for Rosenborg against his former club in the Champions League in season 2001–2002?
12. Who played for Derry City against Gretna in their only European tie and would go on to play for Celtic?
13. Not one Celtic player started every game of the UEFA Cup run in season 2002–03. True or false?
14. In November 2004, Celtic drew 1–1 with Barcelona in the Nou Camp. Who scored Celtic's equalizer?
15. Who played in goal for Celtic in their 1–1 draw in the Nou Camp in November 2004?
16. Celtic defeated Shakhtar Donetsk 2–1 in November 2007 with an injury–time winner from which player?
17. Who scored Celtic's first goal when they defeated Shakhtar Donetsk 2–1 in November 2007?
18. Which Georgian side did Celtic beat 7–2 on aggregate in the first round of the Cup Winners' Cup in 1995?
19. Which French side trounced Celtic 4–0 on aggregate in the 1995 Cup Winners' Cup?
20. Which French striker scored twice in a 3–0 victory at Celtic Park in the second leg of their 1995 Cup Winners' Cup clash?

Answers on page 180

Scottish Clubs in Europe: First Division 2

1. Who did Celtic lose 3–2 on aggregate to in the quarter-final of the European Cup in March 1980?
2. Hopes were raised after Celtic won the home first leg 2–0. Who scored their goals that night?
3. Who was Celtic manager then?
4. Celtic lost 4–2 on aggregate to Barcelona in the last 16 of the Champions League in 2008. Who scored Barcelona's only goal in their 1–0 victory in the second leg?
5. Which French team eliminated Celtic in the second round of the UEFA Cup in 2000?
6. Which Celtic striker scored for Nancy against Motherwell at Fir Park in September 2008?
7. Who did Rangers lose to in the third round of the UEFA Cup in December 1998?
8. Which Rangers defender was sent off in that game?
9. And who gave away a second-half penalty with an inexplicable handball?
10. Rangers played Leeds in a Battle of Britain clash in 1992, with the two-legged tie finishing 4–2 to Rangers. Name the two Leeds scorers.
11. Which player scored the equalizer for Rangers in their home tie against Leeds in 1992?
12. Whose corner led to the goal?
13. Which Rangers player scored the first-leg winner against Leeds in 1992?
14. Who scored the Rangers goals in their second-leg tie against Leeds at Elland Road in 1992, which the Glasgow side won 2–1?
15. Name the two Rangers goal scorers in Lisbon when they beat Sporting 2–0 on their way to the 2007–08 UEFA Cup final.
16. Who did Rangers lose to in the final of the inaugural Cup Winners' Cup in 1961?
17. Which Rangers striker finished joint-top scorer in the inaugural Cup Winners' Cup in 1961?
18. Against which club did Rangers striker Michael Mols sustain a serious knee injury in November 1999 during a Champions League match?
19. Who scored Aberdeen's equalizing goal to make it 2–2 in the eventual 3–2 win over Bayern Munich in the semi-final of the Cup Winners' Cup in 1983?
20. Who scored Aberdeen's winner against Bayern Munich in the semi-final of the Cup Winners' Cup in 1983?

Answers on page 181

Scottish Clubs in Europe: First Division 3

1. How many of Aberdeen's Cup Winners' Cup-winning team of 1983 went on to become managers at top-flight clubs in England or Scotland?
2. Aberdeen drew 2–2 with Bayern Munich in the UEFA Cup in February 2008 at Pittodrie. Who scored the Dons' goals?
3. Who scored the consolation goal for Aberdeen in their second-leg 5–1 defeat to Bayern Munich in 2008?
4. Name any two of the Bayern Munich scorers when they beat Aberdeen 5–1 in 2008.
5. What country did Aberdeen's UEFA Cup opponents in 2009, SK Sigma Olomouc, come from?
6. What was the aggregate score between Aberdeen and SK Sigma Olomouc in the 2009 UEFA Cup?
7. Who scored Aberdeen's only goal over the two legs?
8. What team did Aberdeen scrape a 3–3 draw against (aggregate score 6–4) to qualify for the UEFA Cup second round in 1996?
9. In which year did Dundee United beat Barcelona 2–1 in the Nou Camp in the UEFA Cup?
10. Who managed Barcelona when Dundee United beat them 2–1 in the Nou Camp in the UEFA Cup?
11. Which Swedish side beat St Mirren over two legs in the UEFA Cup first round in season 1980–81?
12. Who scored St Mirren's first-ever European goal in the away first leg?
13. Which French side did St Mirren lose to in the second round of the 1980–81 UEFA Cup?
14. St Mirren were beaten 1–0 by Feyenoord in the first leg of their first-round UEFA Cup tie in 1983. Who was the Dutch side's scorer that night at Love Street, who would go on to become a world-class talent?
15. Who was the Feyenoord manager when they beat St Mirren 1–0 at Love Street in 1983?
16. St Mirren beat Slavia Prague 3–1 over the two legs of their UEFA Cup tie in 1985. Which striker scored twice for St Mirren in their 2–0 home victory in the second leg?
17. Who scored a hat-trick for St Mirren in the first away leg of their second-round tie, which finished 3–3?
18. Despite that, they still went out in the second round. Who beat them?
19. Which Norwegian side did St Mirren beat in the first round of the Cup Winners' Cup in 1987?
20. Which team, who went on to win the tournament, did they lose to in the second round?

Answers on page 181

Scottish Clubs in Europe: First Division 4

1. Who was the manager of Brondby when they beat Aberdeen 2–0 over a two-legged UEFA cup tie in 1996?
2. Who did Motherwell lose to in the first round of the Cup Winners' Cup in season 1991–92?
3. Kilmarnock reached the second round of the European Cup in 1965, but were thrashed by which Spanish side?
4. Which Irish part-time side did Kilmarnock beat in the qualifying round of the Cup Winners' Cup in 1997?
5. Who scored the decisive goal in the second leg in Ireland to take Kilmarnock through?
6. Kilmarnock were outclassed by which French side in the next round?
7. Which Austrian side knocked Livingston out of the UEFA Cup in the second round in November 2000?
8. Which Livingston winger scored twice in the second home leg, once from the penalty spot?
9. Which Finnish team did Dundee United lose to in the second qualifying round of the UEFA Cup in 2005?
10. Which Italian side beat Dundee 3–1 on aggregate in the first round of the UEFA Cup in 2003?
11. Who scored the Dens Park side's only goal in the tie?
12. What was the score when Dundee thrashed Cologne in the European Cup preliminary round in 1962?
13. Name the striker who scored a hat-trick in the home first leg.
14. Which Portuguese side did Dundee beat in the next round of the competition?
15. And what was the aggregate score?
16. Name Dundee's Belgian opponents in the quarter-final of the European Cup in 1962
17. What was the astonishing first-leg score in Belgium?
18. And who scored Dundee's goals in the return at Dens to secure a 6–2 aggregate win?
19. What was the score when Dundee lost to Milan in the semi-final of the European Cup in 1962?
20. Where was that season's European Cup final to be played?

Answers on page 182

Scottish Clubs in Europe: Second Division 1

1. Which club knocked Celtic out of the Champions League in the second qualifying round in 2005–2006 and were then paired with Rangers in the group stages?
2. Who did Aberdeen famously beat in the Cup Winners' Cup final in 1983?
3. Who was the Aberdeen manager?
4. Who was the opposition manager?
5. Who came off the bench to score the winning goal for Aberdeen in the Cup Winners' Cup final of 1983?
6. Who was the former Rangers manager who managed Zenit St Petersburg in the UEFA Cup final against the Ibrox club in May 2008?
7. Where was the 2008 UEFA Cup final held?
8. Who played in goal for Rangers in the 2008 UEFA Cup final?
9. What was the score in the 2008 UEFA Cup final?
10. What was the aggregate score when Derry City beat Gretna in the UEFA Cup in 2006: 7–1, 7–2 or 7–3?
11. Which famous European club, who went on to win the competition that year, knocked Raith Rovers out of the UEFA Cup in the third round in 1995?
12. In which stadium did Raith Rovers play their home UEFA Cup tie against this club?
13. Which manager led Raith Rovers into Europe for the first time in 1995?
14. What feat did Rangers achieve when they qualified for the knockout stages of the Champions League in season 2005–06?
15. Who did Rangers draw 1–1 with at Ibrox on December 2005 to advance to the last 16 of the Champions League?
16. Who scored the crucial goal for Rangers in that final group game?
17. Who was Rangers' opposition in the last 16 of the 2005–06 Champions League?
18. What was the aggregate score?
19. Which Rangers player scored in both legs of the Villarreal tie?
20. Name the Romanian team who consigned Rangers to a 4–1 defeat in the Champions League in October 2009.

Answers on page 182

Scottish Clubs in Europe: Second Division 2

1. Who did Falkirk play on their European debut in the Europa League in July 2009?
2. Who was the Falkirk manager?
3. Who won this game?
4. Who scored Falkirk's only goal?
5. What year did Rangers win the Cup Winners' Cup?
6. Who did Rangers beat to lift the Cup Winners' Cup?
7. Where was the final held when Rangers won the Cup Winners' Cup?
8. What was the collective name given to the victorious Rangers team that won the Cup Winners' Cup?
9. Who was the manager of Porto when Celtic faced them in the final of the UEFA Cup in 2003?
10. Who was the Celtic manager for the 2003 UEFA Cup final?
11. Who scored two goals for Celtic in the 2003 UEFA Cup final?
12. What kind of goals were Celtic's in the 2003 UEFA Cup final?
13. Who was sent off for Celtic in the 2003 UEFA Cup final?
14. In which year did Dundee United play in the UEFA Cup final?
15. Who was the Dundee United manager when they reached the UEFA Cup final?
16. Who were Dundee United's opponents when they reached the UEFA Cup final?
17. What was the aggregate score when Dundee United reached the UEFA Cup final?
18. What is the collective name given to the Celtic team who won the European Cup in 1967?
19. Who did Celtic beat in the final of the European Cup in 1967?
20. Who was the victorious Celtic manager in the European Cup in 1967?

Scottish Clubs in Europe: Second Division 3

1. Who scored the winning goal for Celtic in the 1967 European Cup final?
2. Who was the Celtic captain who lifted the European Cup in 1967?
3. Who did Rangers lose to in the Cup Winners' Cup final in 1967?
4. Who was the losing Rangers manager in the Cup Winners' Cup final of 1967?
5. Who were Rangers' Italian opponents in the 1961 Cup Winners' Cup final?
6. And what was the score?
7. What landmark did Rangers achieve by making it to the final of the 1961 Cup Winners' Cup?
8. Celtic beat Manchester United 1–0 at Celtic Park in the Champions League group stage in November 2006. Who scored a famous free-kick winner with 9 minutes left?
9. Which Manchester United striker missed a penalty moments later?
10. Celtic had lost 3–2 at Old Trafford three months previously. Who scored Celtic's opening goal?
11. Celtic met Manchester United in the group stages of the Champions League in the 2008–09 campaign. What was the score when United came to Celtic Park in November 2008?
12. Who scored Celtic's only goal that night?
13. Who did Celtic overcome in a dramatic penalty shoot-out to qualify for the Champions League group stages in season 2007–08?
14. Who described Rangers' style of play as 'anti-football' after his team had drawn 0–0 at Ibrox in October 2007?
15. Against which French side did Rangers pull off a major shock by beating them 3–0 away in the group stage of the Champions League in October 2007?
16. Which team did Hibs lose heavily to in the first round of the UEFA Cup in the 2005–06 season?
17. What was the shock second-leg score?
18. Which country were the victors from?
19. Who was the Hibs manager?
20. Motherwell lost 3–0 on aggregate to Bordeaux in 2008. Who was the Fir Park manager?

Answers on page 183

General Football Knowledge: Premier Division 1

1. Who were the last winners of the Cup Winners' Cup in 1999?
2. When Paul Gascoigne got booked in the semi-final of the World Cup in 1990, he started crying because he knew he would be out for the final. Who did he tackle to earn that critical yellow card?
3. Who scored the winner for Argentina against West Germany in the 1986 World Cup final?
4. What was Eric Cantona's first professional club?
5. Who said: 'Football is like chess only without the dice'?
6. Who was the top scorer in the 1970 World Cup?
7. And how many goals did he score?
8. Wales have never qualified for a World Cup. True or false?
9. Who won the English Premier League in season 1994–95?
10. At which non-league club did Martin O'Neill begin his managerial career?
11. Which Swiss manager lasted only 9 months at Spurs in 1997–98?
12. Who said: 'It's not nice going into a supermarket and the woman at the till is thinking, "Dodgy keeper"'?
13. Who said: 'Beckham can't kick with his left foot. He can't head the ball, can't tackle and doesn't score many goals. Apart from that, he's alright'?
14. Who won the league as a player for Spurs in 1951 and then won it with them as a manager 10 years later?
15. Who scored England's 5th goal in the 5–1 thrashing of Germany in 2001?
16. Who were joint-top goal scorers at the 1994 World Cup?
17. Who was top scorer at the 1998 World Cup in France?
18. To the nearest hundred, how many appearances did Bobby Charlton make for Manchester United?
19. How many of the 23 members of the England 1966 World Cup squad were 6 feet or over?
20. Name them.

Answers on page 184

General Football Knowledge: Premier Division 2

1. How many caps did Bobby Moore win for England?
2. Pele played most of his career with which club?
3. In what year did the first African Cup of Nations take place?
4. Queen's Park are Scotland's oldest club. In which year were they formed – 1857, 1867 or 1877?
5. In which year was FIFA founded – 1901, 1903 or 1904?
6. Who was voted the first-ever European Footballer of the Year in 1956?
7. Who did Paul Gascoigne commit a knee-high foul on in the 1991 FA Cup final, rupturing his own cruciate ligament in the process?
8. How many times did Johan Cryuff win the European Cup with Ajax?
9. Which player moved from Middlesbrough to Sunderland for the first 4-figure transfer fee in English football in February 1905?
10. Who moved from Sao Paolo to Real Betis for £23million in 1998?
11. What world-record fee did Juventus pay Real Madrid for Zinedine Zidane in 2001?
12. Who became the first black player to win a full England cap in 1978?
13. Who was the first British player to earn £100 a week?
14. Who scored the first-ever Premiership goal in season 1992–93?
15. Who scored the winner for Aston Villa in the 1982 European Cup final?
16. Who did Barcelona beat in the European Cup final of 1992?
17. And who scored their winning goal?
18. Where was the European Cup final of 1992 played?
19. Who scored the only goal for Marseille in the 1993 European Cup final?
20. Who scored twice for Borussia Dortmund in the 1997 Champions League final victory over Juventus?

Answers on page 184

General Football Knowledge: Premier Division 3

1. Where will the 2014 World Cup be held?
2. At which stadium was the 2010 Champions League final played?
3. Who was the manager of Greece when they won the European Championship in 2004?
4. Who scored the winner for Greece in the 2004 European Championship final?
5. Who did Greece beat in the 2004 European Championship final?
6. Where will the 2012 European Championship be held?
7. Who was the first Japanese player to play professionally in Europe?
8. And which country did he play in?
9. Which Italian club bought Hidetoshi Nakata for £18 million in 2001?
10. Name the manager who guided Japan to the last 16 of the 2002 World Cup.
11. Who did Japan lose to in the last 16 of the 2002 World Cup?
12. Who scored twice for Barcelona in their 2–2 Champions League quarter-final first-leg draw with Arsenal in March 2010?
13. Who, in March 2010, said: 'I don't like it (Italian football) and it doesn't like me'?
14. What injury did David Beckham pick up that kept him out of the 2010 World Cup?
15. Who did Neil Lennon appoint as his assistant after being given temporary charge of Celtic following Tony Mowbray's sacking?
16. Which Frenchman took the Cameroon national job in July 2009?
17. What was David Moyes' first professional club as a player?
18. What was David Moyes' first managerial appointment?
19. At which club did Arsene Wenger begin his playing career?
20. What was Arsene Wenger's first managerial appointment?

Answers on page 185

General Football Knowledge: First Division 1

1. Which Brazilian's name translated as 'Little Bird'?
2. Who won the first World Cup in 1930?
3. Who was the first player to be transferred for £1 million between two English teams?
4. What injury did Bert Trautmann sustain, and play on with, during the 1956 FA Cup final?
5. Who is England's record cap holder?
6. How many times have Brazil won the World Cup?
7. Which club has won the European Cup/Champions League the most times?
8. What is Pele's real name?
9. Who signed Dennis Bergkamp for Arsenal?
10. What is Kenny Dalglish's middle name?
11. Which Liverpool manager signed Kenny Dalglish in 1977?
12. What was the fee when Liverpool signed Kenny Dalglish from Celtic in 1977?
13. And what was significant about it?
14. On what Portuguese archipelago was Cristiano Ronaldo born?
15. What was Cristiano Ronaldo's first club?
16. Which team did David Beckham go on loan to for part of the 1994–95 season?
17. Which keeper did David Beckham beat from the halfway line in a league match against Wimbledon in August 1996?
18. Who missed the decisive penalty for Italy in the 1994 World Cup final?
19. Who finished third in the 1994 World Cup?
20. Who managed Manchester United before Sir Alex Ferguson took over?

Answers on page 185

General Football Knowledge: First Division 2

1. Who said: 'There are two great teams on Merseyside – Liverpool and Liverpool reserves'?
2. Who said: 'There's no pressure at the top. The pressure is being second or third'?
3. Who said: 'I wouldn't say I was the best manager in the business. But I was in the top one'?
4. Who signed Frank Lampard for Chelsea?
5. Who did Porto beat in the 2004 Champions League final?
6. Name the Argentinean striker who scored twice in the 1978 World Cup final to beat the Netherlands 3–1.
7. What stage did England reach at the 1978 World Cup?
8. Why did Pickles the dog become famous at the 1966 World Cup in England?
9. What was the nickname of the famous Hungarian national team of the 1950s?
10. Who scored for Northern Ireland when they beat England 1–0 in a World Cup qualifier in September 2005?
11. What was Steve McClaren's next job after being sacked by England?
12. What year was the Munich Air Disaster?
13. When was the first Premiership season?
14. Who was Brian Clough referring to when he said: 'I just don't like him'?
15. Who said of Ryan Giggs: 'I remember when I first saw him, he was 13 and he just floated over the ground like a cocker spaniel chasing a piece of silver paper in the wind'?
16. How many goals did Bobby Charlton score for England?
17. What is Gary and Phil Neville's father's name?
18. Which English club are known as the 'Owls'?
19. Which Liberian was named World Player of the Year in 1995?
20. Who tragically collapsed and died during the 2003 Confederations Cup game between Cameroon and Columbia?

Answers on page 186

General Football Knowledge: First Division 3

1. Which former Real Madrid forward was known as the Vulture?
2. What was the name of Bolton Wanderers' home stadium prior to their move to the Reebok stadium in 1997?
3. Who finished top scorer at the 2006 World Cup?
4. Who scored the final goal for Brazil in the 4–1 destruction of Italy in the 1970 World Cup final?
5. Which player's nickname was 'Mighty Mouse'?
6. Who became the first £500,000 footballer to leave an English club when he moved to Hamburg from Liverpool in 1977?
7. Who scored both goals for Manchester United in the 1991 Cup Winners' Cup final?
8. Who did Manchester United beat in the 1968 European Cup final?
9. Which team used to play at Maine Road?
10. Which English football club's supporters sing 'I'm forever blowing bubbles'?
11. Who said: 'Sometimes you talk about Ronaldinho and Eto'o and people like that; you need to talk about the proper footballer who made the difference, and that was Henrik Larsson tonight'?
12. Juventus are from which city?
13. Who scored Aston Villa's only goal in the 2010 Carling Cup final defeat to Manchester United?
14. What is the name of Aston Villa's American owner?
15. Who knocked Real Madrid out of the last 16 of the Champions League in March 2010?
16. Who won the Coca-Cola Championship in season 2008–09?
17. Who finished second in the Coca-Cola Championship in season 2008–09?
18. At which club did Craig Bellamy start his career?
19. What is the name of Stoke City's home stadium?
20. Who scored Barcelona's goals in the 2–0 victory over Manchester United in the 2009 Champions League final?

Answers on page 186

General Football Knowledge: Second Division 1

1. What age was Pele when he played in the 1958 World Cup?
2. Which Portuguese striker was nicknamed 'the Black Panther' or 'Black Pearl'?
3. Which city hosted the 2002 Champions League final?
4. Who said: 'My history as a manager cannot be compared with Frank Rijkaard's history. He has zero trophies and I have a lot of them'?
5. Who said: 'You can't win anything with kids'?
6. Who won the World Cup in 1994?
7. What is Zinedine Zidane's nickname?
8. Who did Zinedine Zidane headbutt in the 2006 World Cup final?
9. Who said: 'I spent a lot of money on booze, birds and fast cars. The rest I just squandered'?
10. Who said: 'Football. Bloody hell'?
11. Who said: 'If God had wanted us to play football in the clouds, He'd have put grass up there'?
12. Who handballed to score a goal against England at the 1986 World Cup quarter-final?
13. What did the handball become known as?
14. Which team beat AC Milan in a penalty shoot-out to win the Champions League in 2005?
15. Which clubs face each other in the North London Derby?
16. In which country was the 1978 World Cup held?
17. Which commentator said: 'Some people are on the pitch. They think it's all over ... It is now'?
18. Who earned the right to retain the Jules Rimet trophy after winning it for a third time?
19. What is the name of Chelsea's billionaire owner?
20. Whose handball guided France to the World Cup finals in 2010 at the expense of the Republic of Ireland?

Answers on page 187

General Football Knowledge: Second Division 2

1. Which two teams play in the Edinburgh derby?
2. At which club did Wayne Rooney start his career?
3. Who was the England manager before Fabio Capello?
4. Who said: 'When the seagulls follow the trawler, it is because they think sardines will be thrown into the sea'?
5. What was the name of Arsenal's former stadium?
6. Who plays at Turf Moor?
7. Who said: 'Football is a simple game made complicated by people who should know better'?
8. What fictional team did Roy Race play for?
9. What was the score when Real Madrid played Eintracht Frankfurt in the European Cup final of 1960?
10. Where was the European Cup final of 1960 played?
11. Which manager led England to World Cup success in 1966?
12. In which year did the new Wembley open?
13. Which team does former prime minister Gordon Brown support?
14. What is Rio Ferdinand's footballer brother called?
15. Who was the England captain when they won the World Cup in 1966?
16. Who did Manchester United beat in the 1999 Champions League final?
17. Who scored their winning goal?
18. The El Classico derby is played between which two sides?
19. Where do Chelsea play their home matches?
20. Boca Juniors are from which country?

Answers on page 187

HEARTS and Hibs: Premier Division 1

1. Hearts lost the league on the final day of the 1964–65 season when Kilmarnock beat them 2–0. What separated the sides in the end?
2. Which Hearts captain led them to the league title in 1957–58 and also the League Cup?
3. Who was the only team to beat Hearts in the league during season 1957–58?
4. How many times did Willie Bauld win the league with Hearts?
5. How many Scotland caps did Hearts legend Willie Bauld win?
6. How many goals did Alfie Conn Snr score for Hearts in season 1955–56?
7. How many caps did Hearts legend Bobby Walker win?
8. How is Hearts' 1901 Scottish Cup win remembered?
9. Which former Hearts player, from France, had his contract terminated by the club after being found guilty of taking a banned substance in 1997?
10. Who was the last Hearts player to finish top scorer in the league?
11. And how many goals did he score – 17, 19 or 21?
12. Two Hearts players finished top scorers in the league in season 1957–58. Jimmy Wardhaugh was one, who was the other?
13. When did Hearts last win the League Cup?
14. In which season were Hearts relegated for the first time in their history?
15. Who was their manager?
16. Who was his replacement?
17. Who did Hearts sell to Chelsea for £215,000 in January 1979?
18. Which former Hearts manager signed Craig Levein?
19. From what club did Craig Levein join Hearts?
20. Kevin Keegan once played for Hearts – true or false?

Answers on page 188

HEARTS and Hibs: Premier Division 2

1. Where does the club's full name, Heart of Midlothian, come from?
2. Who was Hearts' first captain?
3. Who was Hearts' first non-British player?
4. What nationality was he?
5. Name the Danish international striker who played for Hearts between 1968 and 1970.
6. Who did Hearts face in the 1971 Texaco Cup final?
7. What was the aggregate score over two legs?
8. Which former Hearts striker is now a professional landscape photographer?
9. What nationality was former Hearts midfielder Rudi Skacel?
10. How many goals did he score in his debut season for Hearts in 2005–06?
11. Which former Hearts left-back won the European Championship with Greece in 2004?
12. Who was the permanent successor to George Burley after he left Hearts in October 2005?
13. How long did his successor last in the Tynecastle hotseat?
14. Who joined Hearts from Second Division Arbroath in 2001 and went on to enjoy a distinguished 5-year career?
15. And who did he leave to join in 2006?
16. Who was John Robertson's last goal for Hearts against?
17. Who was Jim Jefferies' first signing after he took over Hearts for the first time in 1995?
18. Who did Hearts face in January 2010 in Jim Jefferies' first game after returning to Hearts?
19. And what was the score?
20. Name the former Juventus and Torino defender who signed for Hearts in November 1995.

Answers on page 188

Hearts and HIBS: Premier Division 3

1. Name three Hibs goalkeepers who have played other sports at a high level
2. Which Hibs left–back was infamously sent off in Gordon Rae's testimonial in 1988 for a late tackle on Gordon Strachan?
3. When did Hibs move to Easter Road?
4. Name the Hibs player who scored the first–ever hat–trick in an Edinburgh derby on 22 October 2000
5. What was the memorable scoreline in that match?
6. Pat Stanton started his Hibs career as an outside–left. True or false?
7. How many Scotland caps did Pat Stanton win – 16, 17 or 18?
8. Name the player who scored a superb 53 goals from 1963 until 1965 at Easter Road
9. Where does the name Hibernian come from?
10. Which Hibs goalkeeper was signed by Pat Stanton for £60,000 in November 1982?
11. Which club did Peter Cormack sign for when he left Hibs in 1970?
12. Who were the opposition when Kevin Thomson scored his first goal for Hibs in the CIS Insurance Cup quarter–final in 2001?
13. At which club did Ian Murray start his career before joining Hibs?
14. What club did Ian Murray play for before returning to Easter Road for a second spell in 2008?
15. Which year did Ian Murray get shaved into his hair before an Edinburgh derby in 2003?
16. What did the date refer to?
17. Who described Hibs legend Willie Hamilton: 'People such as wee Jimmy and Baxter each had that special thing they did brilliantly but Willie could do it all. He could match anyone in the game with his speed, stamina and shooting'?
18. Willie Hamilton won just one Scotland cap. Who was it against?
19. How many times have Hibs been crowned Scottish champions?
20. What is the name of Hibs' north stand?

Answers on page 189

Hearts and Hibs: First Division 1

1. Name three players who have played for both Hearts and rivals Hibs.
2. Who did Hearts lose to on the last day of the 1985–86 season thereby conceding the league to Celtic?
3. Who scored a hat-trick for Hearts in the 1954 League Cup final?
4. Prior to the 1954 League Cup, when did Hearts last win a major trophy?
5. Who was the victorious Hearts manager in the 1954 League Cup final?
6. Who was the youngest player to be inducted into the Hearts Hall of Fame in 2007?
7. Who did Hearts lose to in the 1996 Scottish Cup final?
8. What was the score?
9. Who scored Hearts' only goal in that game?
10. Former Hearts goalkeeper Henry Smith never won a Scotland cap. True or false?
11. Which club did John Robertson leave Hearts to join for a brief spell in 1988?
12. The fee was a club record. How much was it?
13. How many goals did John Robertson score for Hearts?
14. How many goals did John Robertson score against rivals Hibs during his career – 23, 25 or 27?
15. In what year were Hearts formed?
16. Jim Jefferies, the Hearts manager during season 2009–10, once captained the club. True or false?
17. Who is Jim Jefferies' long-term assistant?
18. Which former Hearts striker picked up a Champions League medal with Porto in 2004?
19. Which club did manager Craig Levein join after leaving Hearts in 2004?
20. Who replaced him?
21. Which club was former Hearts manager Csaba Laszlo in charge of prior to taking over at Tynecastle?

Answers on page 189

Hearts and HIBS: First Division 2

1. Who did Hibs sell to Rangers for £100,000 in 1968?
2. What was significant about the fee?
3. Which former Hibs striker was nicknamed 'the Tank'?
4. Which wealthy businessman saved Hibs in 1991 when its owner, the listed company Forth Investments plc, went into receivership?
5. Which trophy did Hibs win in 1991?
6. Who was their manager at the time?
7. Who was the opposition in the final?
8. Who scored the opening goal from the penalty spot?
9. And who scored the second?
10. Who did Derek Riordan make his debut against in December 2001?
11. Which manager handed Derek Riordan his Hibs debut?
12. How many goals did Derek Riordan score for Hibs in the 2004–05 season – 19, 21 or 23?
13. How many goals did Derek Riordan score for Cowdenbeath in their 7–5 victory over Second Division opponents Brechin City in January 2003 during a loan spell?
14. Who led Hibs to the Summer Cup in 1964 and left to join Celtic the following year?
15. Who succeeded him as Hibs manager?
16. Which world-class team did Hibs beat 2–0 in a friendly at Easter Road in October 1964?
17. Name the Hibs' scorers in that game?
18. What age was George Best when he signed for Hibs in 1979?
19. George Best scored on his debut for Hibs. True or false?
20. Who were the opposition when George Best made his debut for Hibs?

Hearts and HIBS: First Division 3

1. How big was the crowd to the nearest thousand for George Best's Hibs debut in 1979?
2. In which season were Hibs last relegated?
3. By how many points did Hibs win the First Division title from second-placed Falkirk in 1998–99: 21, 22 or 23?
4. Which manager led Hibs to the 2001 Scottish Cup final?
5. And what was the score?
6. Name the winger who scored all the goals in a 3–0 Hibs victory over Rangers at Ibrox in August 2005
7. Who were Hibs' opposition in the 2007 CIS Insurance Cup final?
8. Hibs won 5–1 to lift the trophy. Name the two players who scored braces in the final.
9. Who captained Hibs that day?
10. Which manager plucked Jim Leighton from Dundee reserves to sign for Hibs at the start of the 1993–94 season?
11. Name the Hibs player who had an epileptic fit on the pitch before a game with Rangers in October 2002.
12. What age was Scott Brown when he made his Hibs debut?
13. What is Scott Brown's nickname?
14. Who did Alex Cropley sign for after leaving Hibs?
15. Which former Hibs defender moved to Greek side Ionikos on a Bosman deal in 1996?
16. Who scored a hat-trick for Hibs in the 1974–75 League Cup final and still ended up on the losing side?
17. Who did Hibs lose to in that final?
18. What was the score?
19. Which Hibs striker finished top of the goal scoring charts in seasons 1958–59 and 1959–60?
20. What made the achievement even more significant?

Answers on page 190

HEARTS and Hibs: Second Division 1

1. What is the first name of former Hearts midfielder, Locke?
2. Where do Hearts play their home games?
3. In which area of Edinburgh is Hearts' stadium located?
4. Who did Hearts beat in the Scottish Cup final of 1998?
5. Who scored Hearts' winner in the 1998 Scottish Cup final?
6. Who was Hearts' winning manager in the 1998 Scottish Cup final?
7. Where was the 1998 Scottish Cup final played?
8. Who was in goal for Hearts for the 1998 Scottish Cup final?
9. What colour is Hearts' home strip?
10. What is the name of Hearts' city rivals?
11. Who did Hearts beat in the 2006 Scottish Cup final?
12. What division were their opponents in?
13. Who was their victorious manager?
14. Who was sent off for Hearts in the 2006 Scottish Cup final?
15. What was the name of the Russian-born Lithuanian businessman who took over Hearts in 2005?
16. Name the Hearts manager who led the team to the top of the league in his brief spell in charge, before controversially leaving the club in October 2005?
17. Who was Hearts chairman at the time?
18. Which former Hearts goalkeeper won the Scottish Football Writers' Player of the Year award in 2006?
19. Willie Bauld spent his entire career at Hearts. True or false?
20. Which manager led Hearts to consecutive third-place finishes in seasons 2002–03 and 2003–04?

Answers on page 191

HEARTS and Hibs: Second Division 2

1. Who did Craig Gordon leave Hearts to join?
2. What was significant about the fee?
3. Which players became known as 'the Riccarton Three' after reading out a statement in 2006 denouncing the regime of Vladimir Romanov?
4. Two of the three later moved to the same club. Name the club.
5. Name Hearts' Terrible Trio from the 1940s and 50s.
6. Who holds the record for the most competitive appearances for Hearts?
7. As a youngster, John Robertson supported Hibs. True or false?
8. What was the name of the Hearts chairman who proposed a controversial merging of the club with Edinburgh rivals Hibs in 1990?
9. What is Hearts' nickname?
10. Whose nickname was 'the King of Hearts'?
11. Who did Colin Cameron join Hearts from in 1996?
12. Who was the Hearts chairman during season 2009–10?
13. Who said: 'Now it has become obvious to me why you, the monkeys, were trying to ruin Hearts – not only in the championship but in European competitions as well'?
14. Who was former Hearts boss Csaba Laszlo referring to when he said: 'The first time I saw him I thought he was someone from the university who had come to watch us train. Then I was told he was one of our best strikers'?
15. Who scored two late goals for Hearts to rescue a point against Hibs on 2 January 2003?
16. Who scored Hearts' penalty opener in the same game?
17. What was Hearts' winning margin when they beat Hibs in the 2006 Scottish Cup semi-final?
18. Name the Hearts player who scored a hat-trick in the game?
19. Who signed for Hearts in January 2006 for a club record fee of £850,000?
20. Which nationality was he?

Hearts and HIBS: Second Division 3

1. What is the name of Hibs' stadium?
2. In which area of Edinburgh is Hibs' stadium?
3. What is Hibs' nickname?
4. Who wrote the lyric 'I can understand why Stranraer lie so lowly, they could save a lot of points by signing Hibs' goalie'?
5. What song by the same band is played before kick-off at every home game?
6. What was former Hibs goalkeeper John Burridge's nickname?
7. Which former French international joined Hibs in 1999 and later returned to the club as manager?
8. Who is the Hibs chief executive?
9. Who did Garry O'Connor join after leaving Hibs in 2006?
10. And what was the fee?
11. O'Connor became the first British player to play in Russian football when he made the switch. True or false?
12. Name Hibs' Famous Five forward line.
13. How many league titles did the Famous Five lead Hibs to in the late 1940s and early 1950s?
14. Which manager signed all of Hibs' Famous Five?
15. Name the Trinidadian attacker who signed for Hibs in 1998 and played a key role in the winning of the First Division title.
16. Which manager led Hibs to a third-placed finish in season 2004–05?
17. What was the name of the campaign to prevent the proposed merger between Hibs and Hearts in 1991?
18. Name the First Division side who knocked Hibs out of the CIS Insurance Cup in 2008.
19. Which manager led Hibs to CIS Insurance Cup success in 2007?
20. Which club did Steven Fletcher move to from Hibs in 2009?

Answers on page 192

Hearts and HIBS: Second Division 4

1. Name the agent of Scott Brown and Kevin Thomson who fell out with Hibs.
2. For how much did Rangers buy Kevin Thomson from Hibs in 2007?
3. Who did Scott Brown leave Hibs for?
4. What was the fee?
5. What was significant about the fee?
6. Who did Steven Whittaker sign for when he left Hibs in 2007?
7. Who did Hibs face in the 2004 CIS Insurance Cup final?
8. And what was the score?
9. Name the Hibs-supporting Scottish writer who wrote the novel *Trainspotting*.
10. Which former Hibs forward was dubbed 'the Scottish George Best' when he broke through in the late 1960s?
11. Which club signed him from Hibs in 1969?
12. And what was the fee?
13. What was the nickname given to the Hibs team of the early 1970s?
14. How many days did Franck Sauzee's spell as Hibs manager last – 67, 69 or 71?
15. Who was Bobby Williamson's assistant at Hibs?
16. Former Hibs manager Alex Miller won the League Cup with the Easter Road side and also won it as a Rangers player. True or false?
17. What was former Hibs midfielder Derek Townsley's profession prior to becoming a professional footballer?
18. Which manager signed Derek Townsley for Hibs?
19. Which former Hibs striker succeeded Mark Proctor as the club's reserve team coach in 2007?
20. Who made history as the youngest player in SPL history when he came off the bench for Hibs on 24 January 2004 against Kilmarnock, aged 16 years and 79 days?

North of the Tay: Premier Division 1

1. Name the three clubs who amalgamated to form Aberdeen Football Club.
2. Who was Aberdeen's first manager, from 1903 to 1924?
3. Which colours did Aberdeen play in prior to 1939?
4. In which year did Aberdeen win their first major trophy?
5. When did Aberdeen's first league title arrive?
6. Which former Aberdeen defender was named Player of the Year in 1971?
7. To which English club did he move to and how much was the fee?
8. How many goals did Gordon Strachan score for Aberdeen – 89, 99 or 109?
9. How many times have Aberdeen won the League Cup?
10. Name the former Aberdeen player who went on to become a director and played a key role in the club's glory years in the 1980s.
11. Who became the first Aberdeen player to be capped for Scotland, in 1908?
12. Which team did Aberdeen beat in the 1955 League Cup final but lose to in the Scottish Cup final 4 years later?
13. Which player became the first teenager to command a 6-figure fee when Aberdeen sold him to Sheffield Wednesday in 1969?
14. In the 1970 Scottish Cup, name the player who scored the winner for Aberdeen in the quarter-final and semi-final before striking twice in the 3–1 victory over Celtic in the final.
15. What became his nickname as a result?
16. Which prolific scorer did Aberdeen sign from Morton in 1969?
17. Name the Aberdeen player who was sent off in the 1979 League Cup final following a clash with Derek Johnstone.
18. Who did then Aberdeen manager Alex Ferguson sign for £330,000 from St Mirren in 1981?
19. Who scored twice for Aberdeen in the 1989 League Cup final to defeat Rangers?
20. Which Aberdeen player was sent off in their 2–0 defeat to Celtic in the CIS Cup final of 2000?

Answers on page 193

North of the Tay: Premier Division 2

1. In which decade did Dundee United change their colours to tangerine and black?
2. Name Dundee United's leading scorer who was suspended for the 2005 Scottish Cup final.
3. Who signed for Dundee United from Partick Thistle in 2003 but was restricted to three appearances due to injury?
4. How long did Gordon Chisholm last as Dundee United manager?
5. How many times did Dundee United face city rivals Dundee in season 1987–88: 7, 8 or 9?
6. What nationality was Finn Dossing, the Dundee United striker of the 1960s?
7. Who became the youngest player to play for Dundee United in a final in the 2005 Scottish Cup final?
8. How many goals did Eamonn Bannon score for Dundee United – 102, 108 or 115?
9. How many Scottish Cup finals did United reach under Jim McLean?
10. How many did they win?
11. From which club did Dundee United sign Christian Kalvenes?
12. How many players did Craig Brewster hand first-team debuts to in his final match in charge at Dundee United?
13. Out of 30 competitive matches, how many did Dundee United win under Craig Brewster – 3, 5 or 7?
14. What was the score when Dundee United played Rangers in Craig Levein's first match in charge?
15. Which club did Damian Casalinuovo play for before joining Dundee United in 2009?
16. Who made his debut for Dundee United in 1959 and was associated with the club for 40 years, later taking up the chairmanship in 2002?
17. Dundee United legend Maurice Malpas has an honours degree in which subject?
18. Name the player who signed for Dundee United in the summer of 1986 and earned the nickname 'Psycho'.
19. Name the Dundee United goalkeeper who appeared in every match in the 2001–02 season.
20. Which songwriter wrote 'Hamish the Goalie' in tribute to former Dundee United goalkeeper Hamish McAlpine?

Answers on page 193

North of the Tay: Premier Division 3

1. Who did Dundee sign from Derby County for a British record fee in 1950?
2. What manager signed him?
3. Who headed the winner for Dundee in the 1951 League Cup final against Rangers?
4. Which two clubs amalgamated to form Dundee Football Club in 1893?
5. In which year did Dundee win the Scottish Cup for the only time in their history?
6. Who was former Dundee manager Alan Kernaghan's assistant?
7. Out of 38 games under Alan Kernaghan, how many did Dundee win – 9, 10 or 11?
8. Who hit the post for Dundee in the 2003 Scottish Cup final against Rangers?
9. Who did Craig Burley foul to get sent off for Dundee against Hibs in November 2003?
10. Who did Dundee draw with in April 1998 to seal the First Division title?
11. And who scored their clinching goal?
12. What was Dundee manager Jim Duffy referring to in 2005 when he said: 'The unscrupulous world of football has reared its head again and frankly I feel betrayed'?
13. Name the striker who scored in the first 6 games of the 2005–06 season and ended up Dundee's top scorer with 18 goals.
14. Who was former Dundee manager Alex Rae's assistant?
15. Who was sent off for Dundee in their 2–1 defeat to Celtic in the CIS Insurance Cup in September 2007?
16. Who scored Dundee's only goal in the same match?
17. Name the Canadian entrepreneur who took charge of Dundee at the end of 1991.
18. What ill-fated scheme did Dundee spend £800,000 on in 1994?
19. Who was Dundee's top scorer in the 1987–88 season?
20. Who was the surprise appointment as Dundee manager in 1988?

Answers on page 194

North of the Tay: First Division 1

1. Which former Aberdeen goalkeeper created a clubs record in 1971 when he went 13 consecutive games without conceding a goal?
2. Who scored the decisive penalty to win the Scottish Cup for Aberdeen against Celtic in 1990?
3. Which Aberdeen boss signed Charlie Nicholas from Arsenal for £400,000 in 1988?
4. Which striker scored 87 goals in 5 seasons at Pittodrie and then later returned as assistant manager?
5. Who joined Aberdeen from Dundee for £40,000 and a player exchange with Jim Shirra in 1977?
6. Which Aberdeen manager handed Alex McLeish his debut in January 1978?
7. What was former Aberdeen player Arthur Graham's nickname?
8. For which player did then Aberdeen boss Alex Ferguson pay St Mirren £100,000 to be a long-term replacement for Gordon Strachan?
9. Who was Aberdeen's top scorer in season 2003–04?
10. Name the Hungarian international who signed for Aberdeen in 1972.
11. What was the name of Willie Miller's autobiography, published in 2007?
12. Who did Aberdeen beat 2–0 in the 1995–96 League Cup final?
13. Which two strikers scored the goals that day?
14. Which former Aberdeen striker and Moroccan international died tragically in a car accident in 2004?
15. Who took over in goal for Aberdeen following Jim Leighton's injury in the Scottish Cup final in 2000?
16. The 2000 Scottish Cup final proved to be the last match of Jim Leighton's illustrious career. What age was he?
17. Which First Division side knocked Aberdeen out of the Scottish Cup after a replay in 2010?
18. Who scored at the death for Aberdeen to take the original tie to a replay?
19. Which Third Division side knocked Aberdeen out of the CIS Insurance Cup in 2006 on penalties?
20. Where was the game played?

Answers on page 194

North of the Tay: First Division 2

1. Who did Jim McLean succeed as Dundee United manager in 1971?
2. Which club did Dundee United beat in a promotion play-off in the 1995–96 season?
3. Who scored the winning goal for Dundee United?
4. Who were Dundee United's opponents in Craig Brewster's last game as manager in January 2007?
5. What was the score?
6. From which club did Dundee United sign striker Lee Miller?
7. Who made his debut for Dundee United at the age of 16 in August 1990?
8. Who returned to Dundee United after 3 years as part of the deal that took Steven Thomson to Ibrox?
9. Who did Dundee United manager Ian McCall sign from West Brom and appoint as his captain in 2003?
10. Which Dundee United player scored 5 goals in a Scottish Premier League fixture against Morton in November 1984?
11. In which year did Dundee United win their first major silverware?
12. Who did they beat to win it?
13. Who did Dundee United beat in the 1980 League Cup final?
14. Where was this match held?
15. From which club did Dundee United sign Eamonn Bannon?
16. Which Dundee United player won the Scottish Football Writers' Association Player of the Year award in 1985?
17. Who was nicknamed 'the Mad Monk'?
18. From which club did Dundee United sign Morgaro Gomis?
19. Name the full-back who signed for Dundee United from Dundee in 2006.
20. In which position did Paul Hegarty start his career at Dundee United?

Answers on page 195

North of the Tay: First Division 3

1. In what year was Dundee founded?
2. How many goals did Dundee striker Alan Gilzean score in the 1963–64 season?
3. Which club did Alan Gilzean leave Dundee to join in 1964?
4. What was the fee?
5. Who scored the winning goal for Dundee in the 1973 League Cup final against Celtic?
6. Who lifted the trophy as Dundee captain that day in 1973?
7. What prolific young striker did Dundee sign in the summer of 2009, who made an immediate impact?
8. And which club did he join from?
9. Who scored a hat-trick for Dundee against city rivals Dundee United in a 3–0 win in September 2000?
10. Name the player who, in April 2001, became the first Dundee player to be capped for Scotland since the mid-1980s.
11. Why was former Dundee star Javier Artero forced to retire early?
12. Who did Dundee beat in the semi-final of the Scottish Cup in 2003?
13. And who scored their winning goal?
14. Which Dundee skipper was Jim Duffy referring to when he said: 'Every manager he has worked under has held him in high regard and (he) can consider himself unlucky not to have been capped'?
15. Name the Dundee midfielder who moved to SC Freiburg in Germany in 2005.
16. Which Dundee striker scored a hat-trick in a 5–2 win over Clyde in the League Cup third round in October 2003?
17. Who did Dundee lose to in the B&Q Cup final of 1994?
18. Who did Dundee lose to in the 1995 League Cup final?
19. Who did Dundee fail to beat on the last day of the 2005 season only to succumb to relegation?
20. Name the Dundee striker who hit the post in that game.

Answers on page 195

North of the Tay: Second Division 1

1. Name the Dutch goalkeeper who starred for Aberdeen in the 1990s.
2. And from which Dutch club did they sign him?
3. Which striker left Aberdeen to join Middlesbrough in the 2010 January transfer window?
4. Who became Aberdeen's record buy when they paid £800,000 for his services in 1994?
5. Which manager signed him?
6. Which striker scored 87 goals in 5 seasons at Pittodrie and then later returned as assistant manager?
7. Which Dutch international striker scored twice on his debut for Aberdeen against Dunfermline in November 1989?
8. Which former Aberdeen defender was given a testimonial against Everton in 2006?
9. What is Aberdeen's nickname?
10. Who was the Aberdeen chairman during the 2009–10 season?
11. Who became Aberdeen's first foreign coach in 1999?
12. Who became Aberdeen boss in 2002 after a successful spell at Inverness Caledonian Thistle?
13. Who did Sir Alex Ferguson describe as 'the best penalty box defender in the world'?
14. What is the first name of Aberdeen defender Diamond?
15. Who succeeded Jimmy Calderwood as Aberdeen manager in 2009?
16. And who is his assistant manager?
17. Who became Aberdeen's record signing when he joined from Charlton Athletic for £1million in 1995?
18. How many Scotland caps did Willie Miller win – 55, 65 or 75?
19. What is the surname of the brothers Darren and Derek who both started their careers at Aberdeen in the mid–1990s?
20. Who was the colourful former chief executive of Aberdeen who memorably described the Old Firm as 'like two old ladies on Sauchiehall Street lifting their skirts for every league that walks by'?

Answers on page 196

North of the Tay: Second Division 2

1. In what year did Dundee United win the Premier League for the only time in their history?
2. Who was the Dundee United captain when they won the Premier League title?
3. Which club did Dundee United sell Mark Wilson to?
4. What was the fee?
5. Who scored Dundee United's winner in the 1994 Scottish Cup final?
6. And who were the opposition?
7. Who did Dundee United lose to in the 1987 Scottish Cup final?
8. What is the name of Dundee United's stadium?
9. What street is it on?
10. Which ex-Yugoslavian international led Dundee United to the Scottish Cup in 1994?
11. Why did Jim McLean resign from his role as Dundee United chairman in 1994?
12. Who holds Dundee United's all-time appearance record?
13. Which club did Ian McCall manage before taking charge of Dundee United?
14. Who did Ian McCall bring with him as his assistant to Dundee United?
15. Which Swedish striker was Dundee United's top scorer in seasons 1996–97 and 1997–98?
16. Former Dundee United winger Jerren Nixon was an international for which country?
17. Which former Dundee United winger's autobiography was titled, *What's it all about Ralphie*?
18. Who purchased a controlling interest in Dundee United in September 2002?
19. Who took charge until the end of the season after Craig Levein left Dundee United to take up the Scotland job in December 2009?
20. In which position in the league did Dundee United finish in season 2008–09?

Answers on page 196

North of the Tay: Second Division 3

1. Which manager guided Dundee to the 1961–62 league title?
2. Who was Dundee's league-winning captain in 1961–62?
3. What is Dundee's nickname?
4. What nationality are former Dundee strikers Fabian Caballero and Juan Sara?
5. What nationality is former Dundee midfielder Georgi Nemsadze?
6. Which Georgian defender moved to Rangers from Dundee in 2003 for no fee after an SPL tribunal decided that the Ibrox club did not have to pay any compensation?
7. Who began his third spell as Dundee manager in 2008?
8. What was the name of former Dundee right-back Alex Hamilton's 1960s band?
9. What message did Juan Sara reveal on his T-shirt whenever he scored for Dundee?
10. Name the Argentinean keeper who joined Dundee in 2001 and left for Crystal Palace in 2004.
11. Who succeeded Ivano Bonetti as Dundee manager in 2002?
12. What are the first names of Larsen and Sutton who signed for Dundee in 2004?
13. Name the Dundee midfielder who moved to Burnley in 2008.
14. What was the name of Alan Gilzean's son, who also played for Dundee?
15. Which former Hearts and Scotland midfielder joined Dundee in the summer of 2008?
16. From which club did Dundee sign Gary Harkins?
17. Which two Dundee legends have stands named after them at Dens Park?
18. Name the Georgian international who signed for Dundee in 2000 and had previously starred for Newcastle United in the Premiership.
19. Name the Trinidad and Tobago defender who joined Dundee in 2003.
20. Name the Dundee director and Aberdeen fan who ploughed money into the Dens Park club in 2009 with a view to restoring them to the Premier League.

Answers on page 197

Other Scottish Clubs (Including Lower Division): Premier Division 1

1. Which St Mirren player, who would later star for Scotland, became Scottish football's first substitute when he replaced Jim Clunie in a League Cup tie at Shawfield in August 1966?
2. Which is the only Scottish ground to have a hedge growing along part of its perimeter?
3. Who scored a hat-trick for Motherwell against Hibs in 1959 in a total time of two minutes and thirty seconds?
4. Where does the name of McDiarmid Park, St Johnstone's home ground, come from?
5. When did Third Lanark cease to exist?
6. What was Third Lanark's home ground called?
7. Which Morton player was the top scorer in the old First Division in 1978–79?
8. Who scored 58 goals for Morton in season 1963–64 to help secure promotion to the top flight?
9. Who did Morton face in the 1963–64 League Cup final?
10. And what was the score?
11. Which Premier League opposition team did Morton knock out of the Scottish Cup in January 2007?
12. Name the former Morton striker who scored twice in that victory.
13. Who did Morton lose to in the next round?
14. Which player turned out for Gretna when they were in the Unibond League and then later played for them in the Scottish League?
15. Which manager led Ross County to successive promotions in seasons 1998–99 and 1999–2000?
16. Who was Motherwell manager from 1911 until 1946?
17. Which player made 573 appearances for Motherwell during the 1920s and 30s and remained their most-capped player until the 1990s?
18. Who captained the Kilmarnock league-winning side of 1965?
19. Name Livingston's 2003 Brazilian manager.
20. How long did he last – 2 months, 4 months or 6 months?

Answers on page 197

Other Scottish Clubs (Including Lower Division): Premier Division 2

1. Who was the first manager of Inverness Caledonian Thistle?
2. Who did Ayr United beat 1–0 in the semi-final of the League Cup in 2002?
3. Who scored Ayr's goal in the semi-final of the League Cup in 2002?
4. Who was the Ayr manager in the semi-final of the League Cup in 2002?
5. Which club won the Scottish League in the first two years after it was founded?
6. Who became the only Scottish club to win the Anglo-Scottish Cup in 1980 when they beat Bristol City?
7. Who scored the winning goal when Inverness Caledonian Thistle knocked Celtic out of the Scottish Cup in March 2003?
8. Who did Falkirk pay a world-record transfer fee to sign in 1922?
9. Name the three brothers who played for Dumbarton in the mid-1980s
10. Which player-manager led Dumbarton to promotion to the First Division in 1995?
11. In which year were Airdrie United founded?
12. Who scored both St Johnstone's goals when they beat Rangers 2–0 in November 2006 to reach the semi-finals of the League Cup?
13. What colours do Huntly play in?
14. How many times have Huntly won the Highland League – 7, 11 or 17?
15. From which Highland League club did Manchester United sign Steve Paterson in 1975?
16. What is the nickname of Forres Mechanics?
17. Who are the most northerly team in the Highland League?
18. Who were the sponsors of the Highland League Cup during season 2009–10?
19. What street is Dunfermline's stadium on?
20. Which Scottish team plays at Borough Briggs?

Answers on page 198

Other Scottish Clubs (Including Lower Division): Premier Division 3

1. Which player was suspended by Inverness Caledonian Thistle in 2007 after being convicted of possessing cocaine?
2. What was Didier Agathe's first Scottish club?
3. Who was Airdrie's eccentric goalkeeper of the 1980s and 90s?
4. At which Highland League club did Duncan Shearer begin his career?
5. Which Premier League club beat Inverurie Locos 3–0 in the Scottish Cup in 2009?
6. How many times had that tie been postponed previously – 2, 3 or 4 times?
7. Who led Cowdenbeath to the Third Division championship in season 2005–06?
8. Which former Partick Thistle player was voted Scottish Player of the Year in 1981?
9. In which year did Partick Thistle win the League Cup?
10. And who did they beat in the final?
11. Who scored for Thistle in that final and later served as the club's assistant manager?
12. Which team were admitted to the Scottish League when Airdrieonians went out of business?
13. Which Frenchman invested in Raith Rovers in 2004 and took charge of the team for a disastrous 3-month spell?
14. What range of hills are visible from Stirling Albion's Forthbank stadium?
15. What was the name of St Johnstone's previous stadium before they moved to McDiarmid Park?
16. Name the Champions League winner who used to play for Motherwell
17. Who was Alex McLeish's surprise successor as Motherwell manager in 1998?
18. What nationality is he?
19. Name the Hungarian midfielder who became a Dunfermline legend in the late 1980s and early 1990s.
20. What was significant about the fee Dunfermline paid for him?

Answers on page 198

Scottish Clubs (Including Lower Division): First Division 1

1. Who did Dunfermline beat in the 1961 Scottish Cup final?
2. Who was the Dunfermline manager when they lost 1–0 to Celtic in the 2007 Scottish Cup final?
3. Who did he manage before taking over at East End Park?
4. Where did Motherwell finish in season 1994–95?
5. Who was their manager at the time?
6. Who claim to be 'the only team in the Bible'?
7. Who did Livingston beat in the final of 2003–04 League Cup final?
8. Who scored the winning goal for Hamilton Accies when they knocked Rangers out of the Scottish Cup in 1987?
9. Who was Accies manager when they knocked Rangers out of the Scottish Cup in 1987?
10. What did Bobby Ancell's Motherwell team of the 1950s and 1960s become known as?
11. Which club did Ian St John leave Motherwell to join in 1961?
12. Name the two brothers who have managed Motherwell.
13. Why is Motherwell's nickname 'the Steelmen'?
14. Which manager led Kilmarnock to their only league title in 1965?
15. How many years was Jim Jefferies manager of Kilmarnock – 7, 8 or 9?
16. Who was famously, or perhaps infamously, sacked as St Mirren manager in 1978?
17. Who scored the winning goal for St Mirren in the 1987 Scottish Cup final?
18. Which former Kilmarnock forward won the Scottish Football Writers' Young Player of the Year award in 2006?
19. Who was the Morton chairman during season 2009–10?
20. Who was Graham Roberts' assistant at Clyde?

Scottish Clubs (Including Lower Division): First Division 2

1. What was Dumbarton's stadium called prior to the switch to their new home in 2000?
2. What is Dumbarton's new stadium called?
3. Which striker arrived at Kilmarnock in January 2009 and scored eight goals to steer them clear of relegation?
4. Who did Falkirk lose to in the 1997 Scottish Cup final?
5. Who was the losing Falkirk manager in the 1997 Scottish Cup final?
6. Stanley Matthews once turned out for Stenhousemuir. True or false?
7. Who took charge of Falkirk in the summer of 2009 but resigned halfway through the season with the club at the bottom of the league?
8. Which two clubs merged to form Inverness Caledonian Thistle?
9. What is the name of Queen of the South's ground?
10. What is Clyde's nickname?
11. What was the name of Clyde's previous stadium?
12. Where are Raith Rovers from?
13. What was the score when Arbroath beat Bon Accord in the Scottish Cup first round in 1885?
14. Who faces each other in the Ayrshire derby?
15. Who was the millionaire businessman who bought control of Gretna in 2003 and bankrolled their rise through the divisions?
16. Who are the Scottish League's only amateur club?
17. And where do they play?
18. For which club did Owen Coyle leave St Johnstone in 2007?
19. Who was the legendary Dunfermline manager of the 1980s who is now the club's director of football?
20. Which player moved from Hamilton to Wigan in 2009 for a 7-figure fee?

Answers on page 199

Junior Football: Premier Division

1. Name 10 Junior clubs who have flowers or trees in their name.
2. Which now-defunct Glasgow teams played at the following four parks: Rosebery Park, Station Park, Barrowfield Park and Haghill Park?
3. Name the home grounds of the now-defunct Parkhead Juniors, Strathclyde Juniors and Maryhill Harp.
4. If Warout Park was the venue for a final between the Mariners and the Nitten, which three Junior clubs would be involved?
5. How many of Celtic's European Cup winning team in 1967 played at Junior level – 8, 10 or 12?
6. Name six of them.
7. Which Junior clubs did Jim Baxter and Joe Baker play for?
8. Who were the sponsors of the Scottish Junior Cup during season 2009–10?
9. Former Scotland manager Tommy Docherty turned out for which Junior club?
10. Which team has won the Scottish Junior Cup the most number of times?
11. And how many times have they won it – 7, 8 or 9?
12. Which Scottish Junior club ground has the biggest capacity?
13. What is the origin of the Glencairn part of Rutherglen Glencairn?
14. Who holds the record for the number of consecutive Junior Cup victories?
15. Name the club who can lay claim to having made the most Junior Cup final appearances.
16. Why were Ashfield Juniors allowed SJFA dispensation to wear a gold star on their shirt tops?
17. What was the first club to be crowned Super Premier League champions in the West Region?
18. Only two North Region clubs have won the Scottish Junior Cup in the past 100 years. Name them.
19. Name the players who appeared in every one of Auchinleck Talbot's five Junior Cup winning teams from 1986 until 1992.
20. Whose nickname is 'the Whe Ho'?

Answers on page 200

Junior Football: First Division 1

1. In which year was the first Junior Cup final televised live – 1972, 77 or 87?
2. Who was it between?
3. In which year was the Scottish Junior Football Association formed?
4. Sean Connery once played Junior football. True or false?
5. At which Junior club did Spurs legend Dave Mackay start his career?
6. The record attendance at a Junior Cup final was in 1951 when Petershill beat Irvine Meadow. How many, to the nearest thousand, were there – 68,000, 78,000 or 88,000?
7. Which Junior club did Joe Jordan once play for?
8. What is the name of Pollok's home ground?
9. How many times have Tayport won the Scottish Junior Cup – 1, 2 or 3 times?
10. What colours do Kilwinning Rangers play in?
11. Where do Camelon play their home games?
12. Which striker, who went on to play for Celtic and West Ham, started out at Johnstone Burgh?
13. What does the Scots word 'lade' mean in Kilbirnie Ladeside?
14. Which 20-times capped Scotland international joined Linlithgow Rose in 1931 and stayed for a year before joining Hearts?
15. Name the former manager of Maryhill Juniors who went on to lead Stranraer to two successive promotions.
16. Who is the manager of Linlithgow Rose who used to manage East Fife?
17. And which Junior club did he previously manage to great success?
18. Arthurlie once knocked Celtic out of the Scottish Cup. True or false?
19. Name the striker who started out at Arthurlie and played for Dundee, Gretna and other clubs.
20. Which lord do Auchinleck Talbot take their name from?

Answers on page 201

Junior Football: First Division 2

1. Banks O' Dee's home ground has a country in its name. What is it called?
2. Bathgate Thistle reached their first Junior Cup final in 2006 when they lost to Auchinleck Talbot. At which senior ground was the game played?
3. Bathgate were back at the same venue for the 2008 final. This time they won, but who did they beat?
4. And which former Motherwell striker scored their winner?
5. Blantyre Vics won the Junior Cup in1950 but what happened to the trophy?
6. Name the former St Mirren goalkeeper who took over as Cumnock manager in 2006.
7. What is the second name of Junior club Carnoustie?
8. Former Scotland goalkeeper Alan Rough joined which club as player-manager and led them to Junior Cup success in 1993?
9. Which Scotland star of the 1978 World Cup started his career at Irvine Meadow?
10. Where do Shotts Bon Accord play their home matches?
11. Who won the Junior Cup at the third time of asking in 2000, beating Johnstone Burgh on penalties?
12. In which year were the Juniors first admitted into the Scottish Cup – 2005, 06 or 07?
13. Name their first 4 representatives.
14. Name the club who went furthest to reach the fourth round.
15. And who did they lose to?
16. What was the score?
17. Which club are nicknamed 'the Chooky Hens'?
18. Which Junior side are known as 'the Yowes'?
19. Who is the longest-serving manager in Junior football?
20. The Central League Cup trophy was presented to the Central League by which well-known English club?

Answers on page 201

Scottish Rugby: Premier Division 1

1. What was unique about the referee and captains in the opening Test of the 1903 Lions tour to South Africa?
2. Name the Scottish brothers who went on tour with the British Lions to New Zealand and Australia in 1888.
3. Which Scot played his only Test for the British Lions in a defeat against New Zealand in 1983?
4. How many penalties did Gavin Hastings score in the Lions' 19–18 victory over Australia in the third Test in July 1989 – 4, 5 or 6?
5. Which number 8 was Jim Telfer referring to when he said: 'He had natural running ability ... he was also good in the lineout because he was so athletic. But it was his attitude that was so good, he would soak up information'?
6. What unique event happened to Hawick in 2009?
7. Who did David Sole refer to as 'one of the scariest men alive'?
8. Name the former prop who won 50 Scotland caps and spent 32 years as player and coach at West of Scotland.
9. Rob Wainwright, David Sole and David Leslie all attended which boarding school in Perth and Kinross?
10. Who, when asked to name the best Scotland front-row of his time, stated: 'Me, me and me. I thought I was pretty good'?
11. In which year was the Scottish Rugby Union founded?
12. Name two of its founding members.
13. Name the Scotland forward of the early 20th century who was also a Scottish heavyweight boxing champion.
14. The change from a 20-man game to 15 was prompted by a 19th-century petition by the SRU. In which year was the change adopted?
15. Who said: 'Like women, different scrimmaging machines can take time to get used to'?
16. What sport did former Scotland international Gordon Brown's father, Jock, excel in?
17. What was the score when Scotland played France in the opening game of the 1987 Rugby World Cup?
18. How many clubs did Gregor Townsend have in his career – 6, 8 or 10?
19. Name 3 of the countries Gregor Townsend played in.
20. Which Scot's tally of 24 international tries stood as a world record until beaten by David Campese in 1987?

Answers on page 202

Scottish Rugby: Premier Division 2

1. A match between Scotland and Wales at Murrayfield in 1973 set a northern-hemisphere attendance record. What did the crowd number?
2. Name the two Scots who turned out for the Rest of the World against the All Blacks in 1992.
3. The first televised Scotland international was in 1938. Who were the opposition?
4. Who did Scotland beat 47–9 in their opening match at the 1991 World Cup?
5. What was notable about the score when Scotland played the All Blacks at Murrayfield in 1964?
6. Name the Ireland manager who alleged that a Scottish player tried to choke Ronan O'Gara in a Six Nations match in March 2007.
7. Ireland won the Triple Crown by beating Scotland 19–18 at Murrayfield in March 2007. Who scored all of Scotland's points?
8. What was Scotland prop Peter Wright's nickname?
9. What was Peter Wright's original profession?
10. Which club has the greatest number of Border League titles?
11. How many points were Scotland ahead with 3 minutes remaining of their Six Nations match with Wales in February 2010?
12. How many points did Scotland end up losing by?
13. Who scored the winning try for the Welsh?
14. In the same match, name the Scotland player who kicked the ball back to the Welsh from the restart, from which they scored their winning try?
15. Ian McGeechan toured twice with the British Lions as a player. Name the years.
16. Name four Scots who have captained the British Lions.
17. Name the Bath and Scotland second-row who toured New Zealand with the Lions in 1993 and once played as a goalkeeper for non-league Bodmin Town.
18. Who was Ian McGeechan's assistant on the 1989 British Lions tour?
19. Why were there no Scots represented when the British Lions travelled to New Zealand in 1908?
20. Which two players share the Scottish record of international tries scored?

Answers on page 202

Scottish Rugby: Premier Division 3

1. What match was Lions skipper Mike Campbell-Lamerton referring to when he said in 1966: 'I would rather die than go through such an experience again'?
2. Which Scot played all 4 matches on the 1924 tour of South Africa despite not having been capped for his country?
3. What was Paul Burnell's nickname?
4. What university did Gavin Hastings attend?
5. Which Scot was the originator of the seven-a-side game?
6. In what year was the first Melrose Sevens tournament staged?
7. Name the brothers who are widely credited with introducing rugby to Scotland in the mid-19th century.
8. In which year did the first rugby international between Scotland and England take place?
9. Where was the first rugby international played?
10. Who scored the first try in international rugby for Scotland during that match?
11. Who won this first rugby international?
12. Scotland beat Wales 34–18 in 1982, ending a losing streak that stretched back how many years?
13. Who won a then record 52 caps for Scotland between 1972 and 84?
14. Who was Jim Telfer describing in 2010 when he said: 'He was a bit like Robert Burns, an ordinary down-to-earth man who could speak to anyone'?
15. Which Scot was known as 'the Prince among Hookers'?
16. Who was carried shoulder high and proclaimed 'the greatest Scot of his generation' after playing a key role in Scotland's 21–16 win over England in 1938, which secured them the Triple Crown?
17. Name the player who skippered Scotland and the 1962 British Lions.
18. Against which opposition did Gary Armstrong make his debut as a 21-year-old player in 1988?
19. Where do Kelso play their home games?
20. In which year was Murrayfield reopened after a multi-million pound renovation?

Answers on page 203

Scottish Rugby: Premier Division 4

1. What nationality is Glasgow Warriors full-back Bernardo Stortoni?
2. From which club did he join the Warriors in 2007?
3. Scotland lost to Italy in the Six Nations in 2010. Where was the game played?
4. When did the first Celtic League competition take place?
5. Which Scottish team lost to eventual winners Leinster in the semi-final of the knockout stages of the first Celtic League competition?
6. Which year was the worst for the three Scottish teams in the Celtic League?
7. In which season did Glasgow adopt the name 'Warriors'?
8. Which Scot was the top try scorer in the Magners League in season 2008–09?
9. What is the best finishing position of any Scottish team in the Magners/Celtic League and when?
10. Who was the Magners League top points scorer in 2006–07?
11. Who was the Magners League top points scorer in 2007–08?
12. Who finished two points behind Felipe Contepomi as top Magners League points scorer in 2008–09?
13. In which season did the Celtic League change to a home and away format?
14. Who is the all-time top points scorer in the Celtic/Magners League?
15. How many points has Chris Paterson scored in the Magners League – 640, 693 or 751?
16. When did the Celtic League change its name to the Magners League?
17. Who is the top all-time Scottish try scorer in the Magners League?
18. Which Scot has most appearances in the Magners League?
19. Ten teams contest the Magners League – 2 Scottish, 4 Irish and 4 Welsh. Name the 8 non-Scottish teams.
20. Name the Dutchman who plays for Edinburgh Rugby.

Answers on page 203

Scottish Rugby: First Division 1

1. Who scored the fastest-ever international try for Scotland against Wales in 1999?
2. What was the time?
3. Who eventually won the game?
4. How many caps did Tony Stanger win – 32, 42 or 52?
5. Rugby has never been played at Hampden Park. True or false?
6. Who said to Rob Wainwright after he dropped the ball for a third time in a rucking practice: 'Wainright, you're like a lighthouse in the desert – brilliant but f***ing useless'?
7. Who was the first Scot to register a 'full house' of a try, conversion, penalty and drop-goal, all in one game?
8. This feat was achieved in a 32–12 victory for Scotland in 1991. Who were the opposition?
9. Name the former Scotland captain who won a Blue for Cambridge at boxing.
10. In 1999, who became the first Scotland player to score a try in all 4 Five Nations games?
11. How many caps did Gavin Hastings win – 51, 61 or 71?
12. What height is Gavin Hastings?
13. How many times did Gavin Hastings captain Scotland – 10, 20 or 30?
14. How many points did Gavin Hastings score on his Scotland debut in an 18–17 win over France in 1986?
15. What was significant about the achievement?
16. Who kicked 3 penalties in Scotland's famous victory over England to win the Grand Slam in 1990?
17. Who chipped the ball into the corner to set up the decisive try in the same game?
18. Who scored England's only try?
19. And who kicked their only penalty?
20. Edinburgh Accies' annual match against which opposition is the oldest continuous fixture still in existence?

Answers on page 204

Scottish Rugby: First Division 2

1. Who captained Scotland to Grand Slam success against England in 1925?
2. Who scored the decisive drop goal to give Scotland a 14–11 victory?
3. Where was the game played?
4. Who did Scotland lose 68–10 to at Murrayfield in 1998?
5. What age was Finlay Calder when he made his Scotland debut in 1986 – 28, 29 or 30?
6. Who became the first Scot in over 20 years to captain the British Lions in 1989?
7. Who did Scotland beat in the quarter-finals of the 1991 World Cup?
8. Which England player's late drop-goal consigned Scotland to defeat in the last four of the 1991 World Cup?
9. Who scored Scotland's only try in their 21–12 Grand Slam winning victory over France in 1984?
10. Scotland lost 21–18 to the All Blacks in a Test match in June 1990. Despite outscoring the All Blacks by 2 tries to 1, who kicked 6 penalties for New Zealand to ensure victory?
11. Name the former Scotland star who pinched the Calcutta Cup from its pedestal at Murrayfield in 1988 and played rugby with it before returning the damaged goods and earning a ban?
12. Former England head coach Sir Clive Woodward went to school in Scotland. True or false?
13. Which club team did John Rutherford play for?
14. Name the former Scotland international who switched codes to Rugby League in the 1990s to play for Widnes?
15. How did Budge Pountney qualify for Scotland?
16. Of Matt Williams' 17 games in charge of Scotland, how many did he win – 2, 3 or 4?
17. What was the premise behind Matt Williams' Fortress Scotland plan?
18. Name the late commentator Bill McLaren's son-in-law who scored 2 tries against England in 1976.
19. When Scotland beat France in 1995 it ended a losing streak in Paris lasting how many years?
20. What was Damian Cronin's nickname?

Scottish Rugby: First Division 3

1. What is the colloquial name for the reverse pass Gregor Townsend made to Gavin Hastings to claim a last-minute winning try for Scotland in Paris in 1995?
2. How many caps did Gregor Townsend win – 72, 82 or 92?
3. Who was the father of former Scotland wing James Craig?
4. Prior to 2009, when was the last time Scotland beat Australia?
5. Where did Scotland finish in the Five Nations a year after winning the Grand Slam in 1984?
6. Which two Scotland coaches led the British Lions on their successful tour to South Africa in 1997?
7. Gordon Bulloch's brother has also been capped for Scotland. Who is he?
8. Which Scot had his cheekbone shattered on tour with the British Lions in a match against Canterbury in 1971?
9. When was the first time the actual trophy was presented to the winner of the Five Nations – 1973, 83 or 93?
10. Who were the first team to hold it aloft?
11. When did Scotland first get their hands on it?
12. Which Scot captained the British Lions on tour in 1993?
13. Gordon Brown never scored a try for Scotland in 30 caps but scored 2 tries on tour with the British Lions. True or false?
14. Which club has provided the biggest number of Scottish internationals?
15. Name the Scotland stand-off who won his 50th cap against England in March 2010.
16. Where was he born?
17. How does he qualify for Scotland?
18. What offence was he convicted of in 2009?
19. What was the score when Scotland faced Italy in the Six Nations in 2010?
20. Name the Italian who scored three penalties and one conversion against Scotland in the Six Nations in 2010.

Scottish Rugby: First Division 4

1. In which Border town did seven-a-side rugby originate?
2. What is the name of Jim Calder's rugby-playing son?
3. Where do Gala FC play their home games?
4. What was Jim Telfer's day job?
5. Whose nickname was 'the Bear'?
6. Name the French centre who scored 2 first-half tries in France's 18–9 victory over Scotland in the 2010 Six Nations.
7. Name the Scot who moved to Toulouse in 2008 but made just one appearance after his medical showed that he had a heart murmur.
8. Which country does Glasgow Warriors player DTH van der Merwe come from?
9. What is the first name of O'Hare who plays for Glasgow Warriors?
10. And which country does he play for?
11. Whose nickname was 'Mighty Mouse'?
12. What is Chris Paterson's nickname?
13. Sprinters Dougie Walker and Elliot Bunney once played rugby for which club side?
14. Which Scottish rugby club is the oldest in Britain and the second-oldest in the world?
15. And where do they play their home games?
16. Name the captains of the Edinburgh and Glasgow teams for 2009–10.
17. Which competitions preceded the Six Nations?
18. When did the last Five Nations take place and who won?
19. When did the last Home Nations tournament take place?
20. At which two Olympic Games was rugby included as a sport?

Scottish Rugby: Second Division 1

1. Who was the Scotland coach during the 2009–10 season?
2. What nationality is he?
3. Who did Scotland beat 23–20 in March 2010 to avoid the Six Nations wooden spoon?
4. Who kicked 18 points for Scotland in that game?
5. And who scored Scotland's try?
6. Name the legendary Scottish rugby commentator who died in January 2010.
7. Which Scotland winger needed two neck operations after being injured in a defeat to Wales in February 2010?
8. By what score did Scotland beat England to win the Grand Slam in 1990?
9. Who scored the winning try?
10. Who was the victorious Scotland captain when they won the Grand Slam in 1990?
11. Who was the defeated England Grand Slam captain in 1990?
12. Who was the victorious Scotland Grand Slam coach in 1990?
13. Who was appointed Scotland's first foreign head coach in 2003?
14. What nationality is he?
15. What is the Christian name of fly-half Godman?
16. When did Scotland last win the Grand Slam before 1990?
17. Who did they beat in their final match?
18. Which player scored 5 penalties and 1 conversion in that match?
19. And who did he play his club rugby for?
20. Which head coach led Scotland to Calcutta Cup success against England in 2006 and 2008?

Answers on page 206

Scottish Rugby: Second Division 2

1. Who broke the 750-point landmark on the occasion of his 100th cap against Wales during the 2010 Six Nations?
2. Which Scotland forward's father was also an international player?
3. Name the Scotland forward who announced in 2009 that he would not play on a Sunday due to his religious beliefs.
4. Which Finlay won 34 caps for Scotland between 1986 and 1991?
5. And what was his brother called, who also played for Scotland?
6. What position did Craig Chalmers star in for Scotland?
7. At which club did Craig Chalmers begin his career?
8. Name the former Scotland rugby international who appeared in the fifth series of *Strictly Come Dancing*.
9. And who is he married to?
10. What was former Scotland rugby international John Jeffrey's nickname?
11. What was former Scotland rugby international John Jeffreys' day job?
12. Where was former Scotland centre Sean Lineen born?
13. How many professional rugby teams does Scotland have?
14. Name them.
15. What is Rob Moffat's job?
16. Where do Glasgow Warriors play their home games?
17. Who is Glasgow Warriors' head coach?
18. Name the two Leslie brothers who played for Scotland in the late 1990s and early 2000s.
19. Where were they born?
20. Scotland's best finish in a Rugby World Cup was in 1991. Where did they finish?

Scottish Rugby: Second Division 3

1. Who was the chief executive of the Scottish Rugby Union during season 2009–10?
2. In which year did Scotland win their first Grand Slam?
3. Name the cup that is competed for annually by Scotland and England.
4. Name the Scottish and British Lions back-row forward who signed for Stade Francais in 2007.
5. Name the former Scotland international who led Bath to Heineken Cup glory in 1998 and, two years later, captained Scotland to their first victory over England in 10 years.
6. Scotland lost 9–6 to England in the semi-final of the World Cup in 1991. Who missed a penalty for Scotland right in front of the posts?
7. Which song was adopted as Scotland's pre-game anthem in 1989 and first sung before a Five Nations game in 1990?
8. Scotland's record points win came in 2004 at McDiarmid Park. Who did they trounce 100–3 that day?
9. Which legendary New Zealander was Gavin Hastings referring to when he said: 'There's no doubt about it, he's a big bastard'?
10. Who did Scotland lose to in the quarter-final of the Rugby World Cup in 1987?
11. Olympic athlete Eric Liddell once played rugby for Scotland. True or false?
12. Whose autobiography was called *High Balls and Happy Hours*?
13. In 1981, who became the first Scottish player ever to hold the world record for points scored?
14. What was the surname of brothers Iain, Kenny and David who all represented Scotland between 1979 and 1991?
15. Who missed a last-minute conversion against the All Blacks in 1983 that would have given Scotland a historic win?
16. What was the final score?
17. What was legendary Scotland tight-forward Gordon Brown's nickname?
18. Who did Scotland lose to in the quarter-final of the World Cup in 1995?
19. Where was the Rugby World Cup held in 1995?
20. What is the surname of Scotland international Hugo?

Answers on page 207

6. How many top-6 finishes did Jimmy Calderwood lead Aberdeen to in his 5 seasons at Pittodrie?

Answers on page 240

5.   Name this Aberdeen defender.

Answers on page 240

4.   Who is this ex-Dundee United manager who led them to Scottish Cup glory against Rangers in 1994?

Answers on page 240

© DC Thomson & Co. Ltd.

3. Name this former Dundee United chairman who passed away in October 2008.

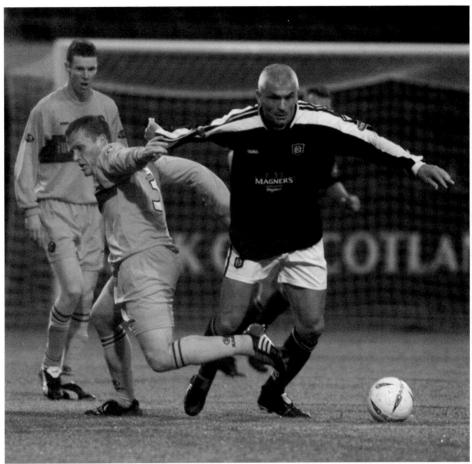

© DC Thomson & Co. Ltd.

2.   Who is this famous Italian striker who played for Dundee in 2003?

© DC Thomson & Co. Ltd.

1. Who is this Dundee legend and captain of the 1962 league-winning side who died in 2010?

© DC Thomson & Co. Ltd.

7.   Craig Brown led Scotland to some major championships. How many?

Answers on page 240

8.   Which Scotland manager handed James McFadden his debut?

Answers on page 240

Scottish Rugby: Second Division 4

1. What is the first name of former Scotland international Doddie Weir?
2. Which club did Andy Irvine play for?
3. What was legendary fly-half John Rutherford's nickname?
4. Which member of the Royal Family is the patron of the Scottish Rugby Union?
5. Which former football chairman was on the SRU's advisory board until 2005?
6. Which Scotland international was in the boyband *Twen2y4Se7en*?
7. Which club did Gary Armstrong join in the late 1990s and inspire to the English League title?
8. Of the 1990 Grand Slam-winning team, Gavin Hastings, Paul Burnell and Derek White all played together for which club side?
9. Traditionally, what is the colour of Scotland's change strip?
10. Who beat Scotland in the quarter-final of the 2003 Rugby World Cup?
11. At which club did Jim Telfer spend his entire career?
12. Andy Irvine never won a Grand Slam. True or false?
13. Which professional club team does Simon Danielli play for?
14. Who kicked 27 points for England in their 42–20 victory over Scotland at Twickenham in 2007?
15. What symbol has been on the Scotland rugby shirt in every game since 1871?
16. Who was the Scotland captain during season 2009–10?
17. What is the surname of brothers Sean and Rory?
18. Name the Scottish professional rugby team which was disbanded in 2007 as part of SRU's cost-cutting measures
19. Where do Melrose play their home games?
20. Against which country did Scotland end a 27-year losing streak with a 9–8 victory in November 2009?

Scottish Golf: Premier Division 1

1. There have been five Scottish Ryder Cup captains. Name them and the years they were captain.
2. What is Eric Brown's singles record in the Ryder Cup?
3. What is Eric Brown's foursomes record in the Ryder Cup?
4. What was unusual about the 1969 Ryder Cup in which Eric Brown was British captain?
5. How many times did golfer John Panton win the Scottish Professional Championship?
6. Name the three oldest golf societies in Scotland in order of their formation.
7. What Scottish course is the longest in Open history?
8. How many Scottish courses have held the Open and name them?
9. Which two Scottish courses have held the Open the most?
10. Which two Scottish courses have held the Open the least?
11. Peter Thomson has won 5 Opens but only 2 in Scotland. Where and when?
12. Tom Watson won 5 Opens, 4 of them in Scotland. Name the 4 courses.
13. Who did Tom Watson beat in an 18-hole play-off to win the 1975 Open in Scotland?
14. On which Scottish course was the first Open Championship held?
15. And in which year?
16. Who won it?
17. And who came second?
18. How many holes did the course have?
19. Name the only 3 men to have won 3 consecutive Opens.
20. Name the Scots-born golfer who emigrated to the US before the turn of the 20th century and won 3 consecutive US Opens between 1903 and 1905.

Answers on page 208

Scottish Golf: Premier Division 2

1. How many times did Sandy Lyle win the European Order of Merit?
2. Who holds the record for the youngest Open winner, set in 1868 when he was 17 years, 5 months and 8 days old?
3. The same player also holds the record for consecutive Open wins. How many did he rack up?
4. In which year was the Open first held at St Andrews?
5. Who won the first Open held at St Andrews?
6. How many times has Musselburgh hosted the Open – 4, 5 or 6?
7. Name the American who won the first post-war Open in Scotland in 1946.
8. And what was his nickname?
9. On which Scottish course did Ben Hogan win the Open Championship in 1953?
10. Which Scot finished third in the St Andrews Open in 1957?
11. On which course did South Africa's Gary Player win the Open Championship in 1959?
12. How many times in total did Gary Player win the Open?
13. At the Centenary Open at St Andrews in 1960, Arnold Palmer lost out by one shot to which Australian?
14. Palmer beat the same player by 6 shots to win the 1962 Open. On which course was it played?
15. Name the American who won the Open at St Andrews in 1964 by 5 shots over Jack Nicklaus.
16. Jack Nicklaus won 3 Open Championships in total. How many did he win in Scotland?
17. Name the American golfer and one-time Open Champion who designed the Loch Lomond course.
18. Which player was 3 strokes ahead with 6 holes to play at the 1982 Open at Royal Troon but dropped 5 shots to fall out of contention?
19. And who took advantage of the late collapse to win?
20. A stake defining out of bounds is regarded as a movable obstruction. True or false?

Answers on page 208

Scottish Golf: Premier Division 3

1. Under the R & A's golf rules, a water hazard must contain water. True or false?
2. Name the Scots-born American who won the Open in 1931 at Carnoustie.
3. The first 4-hole play-off in Open Championship history was held at which course in 1989?
4. The play-off involved 3 players. Name them.
5. Who eventually lifted the Claret Jug?
6. On which Scottish course did Nick Faldo win his third Open in 1992?
7. What club did Paul Lawrie use for his famous approach shot to the final hole in the Open play-off in 1999?
8. Where was Paul Lawrie ranked in the world when he won the Open in 1999 – 100, 149 or 159?
9. Paul Lawrie had finished in the top 10 at the Open before his victory in 1999. In which year?
10. Which Scottish course was Tom Watson referring to when he said: 'This is the most fun I've had playing golf in my life'?
11. Name the former Open Champion who scored a hole-in-one at the 8th hole at Carnoustie in the 1973 Open at the age of 71.
12. In 1939, the R & A limited the carrying of clubs to which number?
13. The Open was staged at St Andrews in 2010. How many times has the championship now been played over the Old Course – 26, 28 or 32?
14. Which two golfers hold the Old Course record of 64 at St Andrews?
15. By how many shots did Tiger Woods win the 2000 Open at St Andrews?
16. How many shots under par did Tiger Woods finish at the 2000 Open at St Andrews – 19, 20 or 21?
17. Name Tiger Woods' two closest challengers at the 2000 Open at St Andrews.
18. Who finished the highest-placed Scot at the 2000 Open at St Andrews?
19. At the third round of the Open at Muirfield in 2002, conditions were so bad that Tiger Woods posted a very high score. What was it?
20. He recovered in impressive fashion in the final round. What score did he post then – 64, 65 or 66?

Answers on page 209

Scottish Golf: Premier Division 4

1. Name the 4 players who were involved in the initial 4-hole play-off at Muirfield in 2002.
2. Name the Brit who birdied 2 of the last 3 holes to claim 4th spot at the 2004 Open, his highest finish in the tournament.
3. Todd Hamilton won his first PGA tour event the same year he won the Open in Scotland. Name the event.
4. What Majors tally did Tiger Woods reach when he won the Open at St Andrews in 2005 – 9, 10 or 11?
5. The earliest-recorded hole-in-one was in 1868 at the British Open on the 8th hole at Prestwick. Who made the shot and went on to win the tournament?
6. What tournament did Colin Montgomerie win in 1989 to announce his arrival on Tour?
7. In which year did Colin Montgomerie win the Scottish Open for the first time?
8. Who overtook Colin Montgomerie at the death to clinch the US Open at Pebble Beach in 1992?
9. Name the player who edged Colin Montgomerie out at the US Open in 1994 and 1997.
10. Who did Montgomerie lose to in a play-off at the 1995 US PGA?
11. In which year was the Open first held outside of Scotland – 1891, 94 or 97?
12. At which course was it held?
13. Which Scottish golfer, when asked in 1991 for his opinion of Tiger Woods, said: 'I've never played it'?
14. Name the Japanese golfer who took a 9 at the 17th at St Andrews in 1978, including 4 shots to get out of the bunker.
15. What Scottish course was Tom Watson describing when he said: 'When there is no wind and rain, this course is like a lady without a dress on – no challenge for a guy'?
16. Name the Scotswoman who won the British Ladies' Amateur Championship in 1937, 55 and 58, and was awarded the MBE for services to golf.
17. Name the Scotswoman who won 7 Scottish titles between 1965 and 86, and the British title in 1981.
18. Name the Scot who won the Italian Open in 1999 and finished 25th in the Order of Merit.
19. Colin Montgomerie made his Ryder Cup debut in 1991. On which American course was it played?
20. Who won the Ryder Cup in 1991?

Answers on page 209

Scottish Golf: Premier Division 5

1. Colin Montgomerie finished third at the US Open in 1992. Who finished second?
2. Montgomerie blew his chances in the third round but what was his score – 77, 79 or 81?
3. Name the two Frenchmen who have won the Scottish Open.
4. Name the Swedish Roger Federer lookalike who won the Scottish Open in 2006.
5. Which South African won the Scottish Open in 2005?
6. In which year was the first Scottish Open held at Loch Lomond – 1994, 95 or 96?
7. Who is the oldest winner of the Open?
8. Which Scot won the first post-war Open in 1920?
9. What odds was Paul Lawrie to win the Open in 1999 before the tournament?
10. Where was Paul Lawrie's first victory on the European Tour in 1996?
11. How many times did Sam Torrance win on the European Tour – 19, 20 or 21?
12. In which year did Torrance sink the winning putt for Europe in the Ryder Cup?
13. Which Scot hit the opening shot at the 1999 Ryder Cup?
14. Where was it held that year?
15. Who finished best-placed Scot at the 2007 Open?
16. In which year were distance measuring devices banned – 1950, 60 or 70?
17. Name the Scot who was born in South Africa but raised in Alloa and finished tied second at the Dunhill Links Championship in 2003.
18. Name the Helensburgh-born golfer who won twice on the European Tour in 2000.
19. What is the surname of Scottish women's golfer Krystle?
20. In 1990, which size of ball became the only legal one?

Answers on page 210

Scottish Golf: First Division 1

1. Who was the first British player to win the Masters?
2. In which year did he manage it?
3. How many Ryder Cups did Scot George Duncan play in – 1, 2 or 3?
4. Paul Lawrie overturned the biggest final-round deficit to win the Open in 1999 – what was it?
5. Who did he beat in the play-off?
6. On which course will you find the Postage Stamp hole?
7. What is significant about it?
8. In which year did Seve Ballesteros win the Open in Scotland?
9. On what course did Seve Ballesteros win the Open in Scotland?
10. How many times did Colin Montgomerie win the European Order of Merit?
11. Of those occasions, how many times did he win it successively?
12. Which Englishman finally ended his run of success in the Order of Merit?
13. What is Sam Torrance's golf-playing son called?
14. Which player, who won the Open Championship in Scotland in 1972, once said: 'You don't know what pressure is until you play for 5 bucks with only 2 in your pocket'?
15. Where and when did Sandy Lyle win the Open?
16. What age was Sandy Lyle when he won the Open – 22, 27 or 34?
17. Who did Sandy Lyle beat by one stroke to win the Open?
18. 'The Duel in the Sun' was played between Tom Watson and Jack Nicklaus on which Scottish course?
19. What was significant about the course?
20. In what year was 'the Duel in the Sun' played?

Answers on page 210

Scottish Golf: First Division 2

1. Name the Australian who won the Open Championship for the first time at Turnberry in 1986.
2. And how many shots did he win by – 4, 5 or 6?
3. Which American did George Duncan lose the 1922 Open to by one stroke?
4. How many Ryder Cups did Sandy Lyle play in – 4, 5 or 6?
5. Which American did Nick Faldo edge out to win the Open at Muirfield in 1987?
6. Which American won the Open at Troon in 1973?
7. Who won the Open at St Andrews in 1990?
8. Name the South African who won the Open at Turnberry in 1994.
9. Name the Swedish golfer who was 2 shots ahead on the 18th tee in 1994, but bogeyed the last hole.
10. Which two players competed in the 4-hole play-off at the 1995 Open at St Andrews?
11. And who won?
12. Name the 25-year-old American who became the youngest Open winner since Seve Ballesteros in 1979 when he won at Troon in 1997.
13. Which Scot said: 'I can remember virtually every shot I have hit in a Ryder Cup. It will go some way towards explaining how much the biennial contest means to me'?
14. What is the name of the burn that crosses the 17th and 18th fairways at Carnoustie?
15. On which Scottish course is there a hole called Hogan's Alley?
16. Name the Scottish golfer who won the silver medal for leading amateur at the 2004 Open.
17. Who won the 2002 Open at Muirfield?
18. And who did he beat in a sudden-death playoff?
19. By how many shots did Tiger Woods win the 2005 Open at St Andrews – 4, 5 or 6?
20. Which Spaniard partnered Tiger Woods in his final round at the 2005 Open at St Andrews?

Answers on page 211

Scottish Golf: First Division 3

1. Name the 25-year-old Dundonian amateur who missed out on the silver medal to another Scot at the 2005 Open at St Andrews.
2. Name the 18-year-old Northern Irishman who shot an opening round of 68 to sit in a tie for third place after the first round of the 2007 Open at Carnoustie.
3. Who missed a 30-inch putt for victory at the final hole of the 1970 Open, leading him into a playoff with Jack Nicklaus, which he lost?
4. Which Scot won the Dunhill Links championship in 2005?
5. In which year was the Royal and Ancient founded at St Andrews – 1754, 64 or 74?
6. Which Scottish golfer's first professional victory was at the Nigerian Open in 1978?
7. How many singles matches in the Ryder Cup has Colin Montgomerie won – 6, 7 or 8?
8. How many Ryder Cups has Montgomerie played in?
9. And how many winning teams has he been part of – 4, 5 or 6?
10. Who did Colin Montgomerie form an excellent partnership with in the Ryder Cup, playing together 7 times in fourball and foursome play, winning five-and-a-half points?
11. What is the burn called which players have to cross to reach the 18th tee at St Andrews?
12. What year did Colin Montgomerie turn professional – 1987, 88 or 89?
13. Name the Scot who won the Volvo PGA Championship at Wentworth in 2004.
14. Which other Scot teamed up with Colin Montgomerie to pick up Scotland's first World Cup in 2007?
15. How many European Tour victories has Colin Montgomerie racked up – 28, 31 or 34?
16. Who did Colin Montgomerie face in a playoff at the US Open in 1994?
17. Colin Montgomerie finished second at the US Open in 1997 when he lost by one stroke to which player?
18. Colin Montgomerie threw away his chances at the 2006 US Open when he double-bogeyed the final hole. Who was the eventual winner?
19. On which course was the 2006 US Open played?
20. The R & A have worked closely with which other association since 1952 to produce a uniform code of rules?

Answers on page 211

Scottish Golf: First Division 4

1. Name the Scot who became the first golfer in European Tour history to rack up 600 tournaments in 1998.
2. Who is the only player to have won the Scottish Open twice?
3. Name the Northern Irishman who won the Scottish Open in 2008.
4. A player is allowed to employ two caddies at the same time during a round. True or false?
5. Which Dane won the Scottish Open in 1996?
6. Who is Colin Montgomerie's charitable foundation named after?
7. Name the Scotswoman who was the first international player to be offered a scholarship at Stanford University, where she attended classes with Tiger Woods.
8. Which Scot finished first on the European Seniors Tour in 2005, 06 and 09?
9. Name the Scot who won the Alfred Dunhill Links in 2004.
10. In which year did Paul Lawrie win the Dunhill?
11. Who was Seve Ballesteros describing when he said: 'The greatest God-given talent in history. If everyone in the world was playing their best, (he) would win and I'd come second'?
12. Who is Paul Lawrie's main sponsor?
13. Who was Paul Lawrie's coach when he won the Open?
14. In 2008, who overtook Colin Montgomerie to become the highest-placed Scottish player in the world rankings?
15. In 2009, who became the first Scot to win a PGA Tour event in America since Sandy Lyle won the Masters in 2008?
16. Name the Scottish siblings who won the Justin Timberlake Shriners Hospitals for Children Open.
17. What is the name of the third brother, who was on caddying duties at the 2009 Open?
18. Who became the youngest-ever Scot to earn a place on the Ladies European Tour in 2009?
19. And what age was she – 17, 18 or 19?
20. Which Scot became the oldest winner of the Volvo PGA Championship in 2001?

Answers on page 212

Scottish Golf: Second Division 1

1. What prize does the Open winner receive?
2. What is the name of the 17th hole at St Andrews?
3. To which course did the Open Championship return for a fourth time in 2009?
4. Which Scot was Scottish Youths champion in 1983 and Scottish Amateur champion in 1987?
5. Which Scot won the silver medal as leading amateur at the 2005 Open?
6. Name the Scot who finished runner-up at the 2005 Open.
7. Name the legendary golf coach and father of Sam Torrance.
8. Which golfer is his most successful client?
9. Where in Scotland was the 2004 Open held?
10. Which little-known American lifted the Claret Jug in 2004?
11. And on which continent did he play most of his golf?
12. Name the South African who finished runner-up at the 2004 Open.
13. Who ended an 8-year drought for the Europeans when he won the Open in 2007?
14. And which Spaniard did he beat in a play-off?
15. At which Scottish course was the 2007 Open staged?
16. Which legendary golf commentator, describing a player's repeated failed attempts to get out of Road Bunker at St Andrews, said: 'My, my, it looks like a couple of Shetland ponies have been mating in there'?
17. Colin Montgomerie grow up playing at which seaside Scottish links?
18. Where is the 'Home of Golf'?
19. Sandy Lyle was born in Scotland. True or false?
20. Name the Scot who sank the winning putt at Oak Hills to win the 1995 Ryder Cup for Europe.

Scottish Golf: Second Division 2

1. Which Scot won the US Amateur Championship in 2006?
2. What is Colin Montgomerie's nickname?
3. On which course is the Scottish Open held annually?
4. What is the name given to a side/team who are as many holes up as there are holes remaining to be played?
5. Name the German who won the Scottish Open in 2009.
6. Spare golf balls in a bag are considered part of a player's equipment. True or false?
7. What is the surname of Scottish women's golfer Catriona?
8. Which major did she pick up in 2009?
9. And at which course was it played?
10. What is the surname of Scottish women's golfer Janice?
11. On which Scottish course was the 2009 Open held after an absence of 15 years?
12. Which American golfer lost in a playoff in 2009, 32 years after he won his first Open at the same venue?
13. And who beat him in the play-off?
14. What fate did Tiger Woods suffer at the 2009 Open?
15. Name the 3 Scottish courses over which the Alfred Dunhill Links Championship is played.
16. Colin Montgomerie has never won the Dunhill Links. True or false?
17. Which football team does Paul Lawrie support?
18. What type of car did Paul Lawrie buy after winning the Open?
19. At which Scottish golf course was Colin Montgomerie married in 2008?
20. A player is permitted to strike the ball with the grip end of his club. True or false?

Answers on page 213

Scottish Cricket: Premier Division 1

1. Name the Helensburgh-born player who made his England Test debut as a spinner against Australia in 1993.
2. And who was he brought in to replace?
3. Name the Scot who captained England 19 times in 28 Tests and hit 4 Test centuries.
4. And which two English County sides did he play for?
5. He was involved in a major cricket controversy in 2001–02. What was it?
6. Which Scottish cricket club broke new ground by employing a Bermudan as their professional in 1934?
7. And what was his name?
8. In which year of the 19th century did Scotland beat Australia at cricket?
9. Name the captain, opening batsman and wicket keeper who led them to victory.
10. Scotland needed 11 runs off the last over to beat an Australian side in 1981, but who was the unlikely bowling hero who dismissed 3 Scots for a duck?
11. Name one of Ayr's greatest-ever players who won 42 caps for Scotland and became captain in 1956.
12. Which famous Scottish author and dramatist wrote this description of an English cricket match: 'A rural cricket match in buttercup time, seen and heard through the trees. It is sure the loveliest scene in England and the most disarming sound'?
13. Who became the youngest player to be capped for Scotland at cricket for 106 years when he played his first international in 1996?
14. In 1956, who scored Scotland's first century against Australia since 1921?
15. Don Bradman's last innings in Britain was in Scotland. Where?
16. How many did he score not out – 103, 113 or 123?
17. In which year did a Scottish cricket team first enter the Commonwealth Games?
18. And who did they draw with in their first game?
19. Scotland lost their next two matches. To which opponents?
20. Who was Scotland's outstanding player in their first season in the English National Cricket League in 2003, taking 25 wickets?

Answers on page 213

Scottish Cricket: Premier Division 2

1. Name the player who scored 164 in his first international cricket innings for Australia against England in 1929 yet was born in Glasgow.
2. Which former Heriot's player made 63 appearances for Scotland, was awarded an MBE and retired in 1994?
3. Who were the first winners of the East of Scotland League when it was formed in 1953?
4. Which English County side did Scotland beat in May 1990 in the Benson and Hedges Cup?
5. Name the overseas professional who helped Scotland to victory and also played his domestic cricket with Greenock.
6. Which club were the first winners of the Western Union in 1893 and won it again in their centenary year in 1993, making it 16 times in all?
7. Name the Greenock cricketer who scored 49 centuries in his career and won 33 Scotland caps from 1913 until 1933.
8. Name the ex-Murrayfield player who spent most of his career playing in goal at Raith Rovers and played in Europe for Hearts.
9. Which club won the Borders League in 1997 for the first time ever?
10. Which cricket club's first honour came in 1981 when they won the North of Scotland Cup?
11. In which year was the Scottish Cricket Union – now Cricket Scotland – founded in its modern form – 1909, 19 or 29?
12. Strathmore and Grange played each other in the 1992 Scottish Cup final. Who won?
13. How many times did Scot Symon, the ex-Rangers manager, play cricket for Scotland – 4, 5 or 6 times?
14. Which Scottish cricket team did future Prime Minister Sir Alec Douglas-Home appear for once in the 1920s?
15. Name the 3 stars of the all-conquering West Indies side of the 1980s who have played for Scotland.
16. In which year of the 18th century was the first game of cricket played in Scotland?
17. And where did it take place?
18. How was it introduced to Scotland?
19. Which Scot was named in England's one-day squad for their tour of India in 1998?
20. And who did he coach at the 2003 World Cup?

Answers on page 214

Scottish Cricket: First Division 1

1. Name the Falkirk-born cricketer who signed for Essex and opened the batting for years alongside Graham Gooch.
2. How many county championships did he win with Essex – 4, 5 or 6?
3. How many times did Andy Goram represent Scotland at cricket?
4. Name the future England Test player who was bowled by Andy Goram in a Natwest Trophy game against Yorkshire in 1989.
5. Which club won the Scottish Counties Championship 8 times between 1975 and 95, including 3 times in a row from 1986–88?
6. Name the player who made his debut for Scotland against the touring Indians at Myreside in May 1946, scoring 59, and went on to play 50 first-class matches for Scotland until 1963.
7. What was his profession?
8. Name the Lahore-born player who played for Scotland and was man-of-the-match in the Benson and Hedges Cup game against Yorkshire in 1998.
9. And why was he banned from cricket for a year in 2005?
10. Which Scottish cricket club play in England?
11. Name the much-respected Scottish umpire who died in 1995, the same year he umpired his last big game (Scotland–West Indies).
12. Name the team who were promoted from East of Scotland Division 3 to Division 1 in successive seasons from 1993–1995.
13. Name the Helensburgh-born player who learned most of his cricket in Australia, played for Essex and made several appearances for Scotland in the late 1990s and 2000s.
14. Name the National League team whose overseas professionals have included Pakistani internationals Shahid Saeed, Akram Raza and Basit Ali, and Indian Surender Khanna.
15. Where is Watsonians Cricket Club based?
16. Which Scottish team plays on the beach?
17. Which Celtic player once captained the Scotland under-15 cricket team?
18. How many Test matches did Gavin Hamilton play for England?
19. Who were Scotland's two group opponents in the 2009 ICC World Twenty20 World Cup?
20. Where did Scotland finish in the 3-team group?

Scottish Cricket: First Division 2

1. Name the Scottish cricket club who won the National Village Cup in 1985.
2. Who did they beat to lift the trophy?
3. Who was their winning captain?
4. And what did he have named in his honour following this victory?
5. In which year was Scotland's first win over an English county – 1949, 59 or 69?
6. Which cricket team regained the Border League in 1996 – their 30th success – after not winning it since 1975?
7. Which cricket team won a Scottish league and cup double in 1997?
8. Which English county did Scotland beat in a Benson and Hedges Cup match in Perth in 1986?
9. Who did Scotland beat in a third-place play-off in the ICC Trophy in 1997 to qualify for the 1999 World Cup?
10. Scotland's first-ever win over an English County in the NatWest Trophy came in 1998. Who did they beat?
11. Name the Jamaican who was the professional at Stirling County for 9 years.
12. Which cricket club plays at Inchture ground near Dundee?
13. And name the former Dundee United goalkeeper who used to play for them.
14. Name the famous Stenhousemuir batsman who scored 27,588 runs in club cricket in a career running from 1955 until 1992.
15. Who did Scotland beat in the final to win the 2005 ICC Trophy?
16. In which year did Scotland win the inaugural ICC Intercontinental Cup?
17. Who did they beat in the final?
18. And who scored 115 runs in the final to secure an easy victory?
19. Who became Scotland's youngest-capped cricketer since 1890 when he won his first cap in 1996?
20. And which Scottish league side was he due to sign for in 2007 only for it to fall through?

Answers on page 215

Scottish Cricket: Second Division

1. What is the collective name for Scotland's national cricket team?
2. Which club plays at Langloan?
3. Which world-class Indian cricketer played for Scotland as an overseas professional in 2003?
4. And how many centuries did he score – 2, 3 or 4?
5. This Indian legend played in 11 National League games against English counties. How many times did he end up on the winning side?
6. Where is Clydesdale Cricket Club based?
7. How many times have Clydesdale Cricket Club won the National Cricket League since 1998 – 1, 2 or 3 times?
8. Where is Carlton Cricket Club based?
9. Who was the Scotland cricket captain in 2010?
10. Who was the chief executive of Cricket Scotland in 2010?
11. What is the first name of Lockhart who has played over 100 times at cricket for Scotland?
12. Who is the highest-capped Scottish cricket player?
13. And whose record did he overtake in 2006?
14. Name Scotland's 3 group opponents at the 2007 Cricket World Cup.
15. Out of their 3 matches, how many did Scotland win at the 2007 Cricket World Cup?
16. Where was the tournament held?
17. Former Rangers captain Terry Butcher turned out for Stirling County occasionally in the mid-1990s. True or false?
18. Which Borders cricket club is believed to be the oldest in Scotland?
19. In which city are the headquarters of Cricket Scotland based?
20. Who was the chairman of Cricket Scotland in 2010?

Scottish Athletics: Premier Division 1

1. What age was Allan Wells when he won Olympic gold at Moscow in 1980?
2. Allan Wells set a Scottish and British record in the second round of the 100 metres at the 1980 Olympics. What time did he run?
3. At which discipline was Allan Wells Scottish Junior champion in 1970?
4. What was Eric Liddell's middle name?
5. What colour of medal did Eric Liddell win in the 200 metres at the Paris Olympics in 1924?
6. Which American sprinter won gold?
7. Who was the last British sprinter to win a 100 metres Olympic medal prior to Allan Wells?
8. Who beat Allan Wells to the 200 metres title in Moscow 1980?
9. In which English city was Scottish runner Ian Stewart born?
10. Name the English club Scottish runner Ian Stewart ran for.
11. In which city did Ian Stewart win the 5000 metres European title in June 1970?
12. Who did Ian Stewart beat to the 5000 metres Scottish title in 1970?
13. What records did Ian Stewart set in winning the 5000 metres Commonwealth title in 1970?
14. Which Scot took the silver in the 5000 metres final at the 1970 Commonwealth Games?
15. And name the Kenyan who finished third.
16. In the 5000 metres at the Commonwealth Games in 1974, where did Ian Stewart finish?
17. Where did Ian Stewart finish in the 10,000 metres at the Commonwealth Games in 1974?
18. Who edged Allan Wells into second place in the 100 metres at the 1978 Commonwealth Games?
19. What colour of medal did Allan Wells win in the 200 metres at the 1978 Commonwealth Games?
20. How many gold medals did Allan Wells win at the 1982 Commonwealth Games in Brisbane?

Answers on page 216

Scottish Athletics: Premier Division 2

1. How many medals did Scotland win at the 1970 Commonwealth Games in Edinburgh – 20, 25 or 30?
2. Where did Scotland finish in the medals table at the 1970 Commonwealth Games in Edinburgh – 4th, 5th or 6th?
3. Name Scotland and Britain's first Olympic gold medallist.
4. Who beat Liz McColgan to gold in the 10,000 metres at the 1988 Olympics?
5. In which position did Liz McColgan finish in the 10,000 metres final at the Barcelona Olympics in 1992 – 5th, 6th or 7th?
6. Where did Liz McColgan finish in the marathon at the 1996 Olympics – 14th, 15th or 16th?
7. What colour of medal did Yvonne Murray win in the 3000 metres at the European Championships in 1986?
8. Name the Scotsman who won the country's first Olympic track gold in 1908.
9. Over which distance did he win?
10. What was unique about the manner of his victory?
11. Name the Scot who took silver in the 1500 metres final at the Athens interim Olympics in 1906.
12. Which Scotsman won gold in the 3-mile team race at the 1908 Olympics?
13. Why did Tom McKean fail to reach the final of the 800 metres at the Seoul Olympics in 1988?
14. In which position did Tom McKean finish in the 800 metres final at the 1987 World Championships?
15. Tom McKean won a silver medal at the 1990 Commonwealth Games in Auckland. In which event?
16. In which city was Tom McKean crowned World Indoor 800 metres Champion in 1993?
17. In which city did Tom McKean become European Indoor 800 metres Champion in 1990?
18. Tom McKean won gold at the European Championships in 1990. Which Brit finished second?
19. And in which city did the championships take place?
20. Name the athlete who, at the age of 15, became the youngest-ever member of a Scottish Commonwealth Games team in Manchester in 2002.

Answers on page 216

Scottish Athletics: Premier Division 3

1. Cameron Sharp won gold for Scotland at the 1978 Commonwealth Games in Edmonton in the 4 x 100 metres relay. Name the other 3 members of the relay team.
2. Cameron Sharp picked up three medals of the same colour at the 1982 Commonwealth Games in Brisbane. What colour?
3. Cameron Sharp's daughter is a promising 800 metres runner. What is her name?
4. Name the Scot who was understudy to Paula Radcliffe for the Olympic marathon in Beijing in 2008 but failed to get the call-up despite the latter being hampered by injury.
5. Name the Scot who held the British 100 metres record between 1967 and 1974.
6. And what profession did he enter thereafter?
7. Name the Scot who beat Steve Cram in the Moscow Olympic trial but missed out on the 1980 Games when selectors controversially awarded a retrial.
8. Name the Scot who finished 6th in the 3000 metres Steeplechase at the 1992 Olympics.
9. Who was the first Scot to long jump over 8 metres?
10. Who is the Scottish hammer women's record holder?
11. She appears on TV under a different name. What is it?
12. Who is the men's Scottish record holder at 60 metres hurdles?
13. Which colour of medal did Chris Baillie win in the 110 metres hurdles at the 2006 Commonwealth Games?
14. And whose national record did he beat in the process?
15. How many medals did Scotland win at the 2006 Commonwealth Games – 28, 29 or 30?
16. Where did Scotland finish on the overall medals table at the 2006 Commonwealth Games – 6th, 7th or 8th?
17. Name the Scottish athlete who became the first to achieve a qualification standard for the Delhi Commonwealth Games 2010 when he threw a Scottish record in the javelin at the British University Championships.
18. How far did he throw to the nearest metre – 75, 76 or 77 metres?
19. Name the Scot who broke the women's Scottish triple jump record in 2007.
20. Name the 1500 metres World Junior Champion who switched nationality to compete for Scotland in 2009.

Answers on page 217

Scottish Athletics: First Division 1

1. What was the name of the stadium in which Allan Wells won Olympic gold in 1980?
2. What lane was Allan Wells drawn in for the 1980 Olympic 100 metres final?
3. What was Allan Wells' winning time in the 1980 Olympic 100 metres final?
4. Which athlete did Allan Wells beat to gold in a photo finish in the 1980 Olympic 100 metres final?
5. Which nationality was the silver medallist in the 1980 Olympic 100 metres final?
6. Who was the last British sprinter to win 100 metres Olympic gold prior to Allan Wells?
7. In June 1969, Ian Stewart and his older sibling became the first brothers in the world to break the 4-minute barrier for the one mile. What was Ian's brother's name?
8. What was the name of Ian Stewart's sister who was crowned Commonwealth Games 1500 metres Champion in 1978?
9. In which year did Ian Stewart win the World Cross-Country title – 1974, 75 or 76?
10. What colour of medal did Ian Stewart win in the 5000 metres at the 1972 Olympics in Munich?
11. Where did Ian Stewart finish in the 5000 metres final at the Montreal Olympics – 5th, 6th or 7th?
12. In which country was Eric Liddell born?
13. What kind of work did Eric Liddell pursue after athletics?
14. Name the Scot who won the 10,000 metres title at the 1970 Commonwealth Games.
15. Which Scotswoman won the 800 metres title in 1970?
16. And which Scotswoman claimed gold in the discus?
17. Why did 32 countries boycott the 1986 Commonwealth Games in Edinburgh?
18. Name the Scotswoman who won gold in the 10,000 metres at the 1986 Commonwealth Games in Edinburgh.
19. In which city did she also win gold at the 1991 World Championships?
20. At which American University did she study?

Scottish Athletics: First Division 2

1. Which Scotswoman took bronze in the 3000 metres at the Commonwealth Games in 1986?
2. And which colour of medal did she win over the same distance at the Seoul Olympics two years later?
3. Name the Scot who was European Champion in 200 metres and 4 x 100 metres Relay in 1998.
4. What was Tom McKean's nickname?
5. Who beat Tom McKean to gold in the 800 metres final at the 1986 Commonwealth Games?
6. Which two track legends did Tom McKean split in the 800 metres final at the 1986 European Championships?
7. In which city did that famous race take place?
8. Who was Tom McKean's coach?
9. How many successive European Cup titles did Tom McKean win – 2, 3 or 4?
10. Name the Scots-born woman who won the Modern Pentathlon at the 2000 Sydney Olympics.
11. Who was the first-home Scot to break the 4-minute mile in 1969?
12. Name the Glasgow-born athlete who just missed out on bronze in the 100 metres at the 1948 London Olympics after photofinish technology was used.
13. Which event did Lee McConnell compete in before turning to track running?
14. In which event did Lee McConnell win bronze at the 2006 Commonwealth Games in Melbourne?
15. And in which different event did she claim another bronze in the World Championships in Osaka the following year?
16. Name the Scottish sprinter who reached the Olympic 100 metres semi-final in 1996.
17. Name the Scotswoman who competed in the 400 metres Hurdles at the Sydney Olympics but failed to get beyond the first round.
18. Which Scotswoman won silver in the 400 metres at the 1998 Commonwealth Games?
19. Name the Scot who claimed a silver medal in the 4 x 100 metres Relay at the Seoul Olympics in 1988.
20. Name the Scotswoman who won the 400 metres for Great Britain at the European Cup in 1995 and whose father was a goalkeeper for Rangers.

Answers on page 218

Scottish Athletics: Second Division

1. In which Scottish city were the 1970 Commonwealth Games held?
2. What was the name of the film that portrayed Eric Liddell's achievements at the 1924 Paris Olympics?
3. At which sport did Eric Liddell represent Scotland before he took up athletics?
4. Over which distance did Eric Liddell refuse to run at the 1924 Paris Olympics?
5. Why?
6. Over which distance did Liddell compete instead?
7. What colour of medal did he win?
8. What was significant about his time?
9. Which Scottish city will host the Commonwealth Games in 2014?
10. Which city submitted a rival bid?
11. Which Scottish city does Liz McColgan come from?
12. What is the name of Liz McColgan's husband, a former steeplechaser from Northern Ireland?
13. Name McColgan's daughter, who is also an athlete.
14. Which marathon did Liz McColgan win in 1991?
15. What profession did Tom McKean move into after athletics?
16. Name the Scotswoman who picked up a 400 metres silver in the Commonwealth Games in Manchester in 2002 and also won a European Championship bronze the same season.
17. Name the endurance runner born in St Andrews who was the only male Scot named by Great Britain for an individual event at the World Athletics Championships in Osaka in 2007.
18. Who was the only Scotswoman selected for an individual event at the World Athletics Championships in Osaka in 2007?
19. Name the Scot who won a 4 x 400 metres relay bronze at the Moscow Olympics at the age of 16.
20. And who coached her?

Answers on page 218

Scottish Horseracing: Premier Division 1

1. Which Scottish trainer won the 2000 Guineas with Rockavon in 1961?
2. How many Oaks winners did Willie Carson ride – 2, 3 or 4?
3. How many St Leger winners did Willie Carson win?
4. Who did Willie Carson serve his jockey's apprenticeship under?
5. In which year did Willie Carson win the Derby for the first time?
6. What was the name of the horse on which Willie Carson won the Derby for the first time?
7. Willie Carson won his second Derby in 1980 on which horse?
8. What age was Willie Carson when he retired – 50, 54 or 58?
9. Which Scot won the 1000 Guineas in 1968 and finished runner-up to Lester Piggott in the Jockeys Championship?
10. Where did he finish in the Derby the following season?
11. What age was he then – 19, 20 or 21?
12. Who both trained and jockeyed the winner of the 2006 Scottish Grand National?
13. Name the horse that won the 2006 Scottish Grand National.
14. In which year was the first Scottish Grand National run?
15. Which horse won the Scottish National in 1911, 12 and 13?
16. And name the horse that also won it 3 times, in 1934, 36 and 39.
17. Name the first Scottish-trained winner of the Grand National (1979).
18. And who was the trainer?
19. Who trained two Ayr Gold Cup winners, Swinging Junior in 1972 and Roman Warrior in 75?
20. The 1989 St Leger had a Scottish connection – what was it?

Answers on page 219

Scottish Horseracing: Premier Division 2

1. Which horse won the Cheltenham Champion Hurdle and a race at Hamilton in 1980?
2. Which Scots-born classic-winning trainer has the stable motto 'Always Trying'?
3. Which Scottish racecourse was the first in Britain to hold an evening meeting?
4. Which Scottish-trained horse won the 1994 County Hurdle at the Cheltenham Festival?
5. Which John Wilson-trained horse won the 1985 running of the Supreme Novices Hurdle at the Cheltenham Festival?
6. What is the Ayrshire connection with the 1888 Derby?
7. On which horse did Richard Quinn win the Epsom Oaks in 2000?
8. Name either of Len Lungo's two winners at the Cheltenham Festival.
9. At which famous Scottish race meeting is the Saints and Sinners charity night staged?
10. In which month is the Scottish National traditionally run?
11. Paris Pike won the Scottish National in 2000. Who was the jockey?
12. Which horse did Tony McCoy win the Scottish National on in 1997?
13. Who trained the 1997 Scottish National winner?
14. How many times did Peter Scudamore win the Scottish National – 1, 2 or 3 times?
15. Name one of the horses he won on.
16. Which Sean Curren-trained horse won the Scottish National in 2008?
17. How many times was Willie Carson Champion Jockey – 4, 5 or 6 times?
18. And name the years.
19. Name the Scottish businessman, steward and racecourse director who said: 'I consider a successful owner to be one who either breeds or buys winners. Just owning a lot of horses probably means throwing money down the drain.'
20. Name the horse that won the Scottish National in 2002 that was ridden by Ruby Walsh and trained by Martin Pipe.

Answers on page 219

Scottish Horseracing: First Division 1

1. Who trained three winners of the Scottish Grand National in 1972, 77 and 81?
2. Which Scottish trainer trained five winners of the Scottish National?
3. Name three of the five.
4. On which horse did he also ride the winner?
5. By what nickname was he better known?
6. Name the Scottish brothers who rode their first winners while still at school in the early 1950s and continued to compete into the late 1980s.
7. How many Derby winners did Willie Carson ride?
8. In which year did Willie Carson become Champion Jockey for the first time – 1972, 74 or 78?
9. In which year did Willie Carson ride his first winner – 1962, 68 or 72?
10. On which horse did Willie Carson win the 2000 Guineas in 1972?
11. Who was Willie Carson speaking about when he said: 'I seemed doomed to play second fiddle to him forever'?
12. What was the original venue for the Scottish National?
13. Which horse won the Scottish National in 2009?
14. Who was the winning jockey?
15. In 2007, which jockey rode the winner of the Scottish National and also took part in the Ayr Gold Cup?
16. Name the jockey who won the Scottish National in both 1998 and 2000.
17. Name the horse that won the Scottish National in 1953, 54 and 56.
18. Which horse won the Scottish National in 1987 and the Grand National in 1989?
19. And which horse did the same double in 1994 and 1998?
20. Name the famous stables in Ayr that are associated with jockeys such as Lester Piggott and Pat Eddery who have ridden horses from there.

Answers on page 220

Scottish Horseracing: First Division 2

1. Who once said: 'Scottish racegoers are the worst in the world. I get abused and shouted at every time I lose on a horse there'?
2. Which trainer of four Derby winners was born in Aberdeen?
3. What is the Ayr Gold Cup's claim to fame in European racing?
4. Two women have trained a Scottish Grand National winner. Name them.
5. Only one Scottish jump jockey has won more than 1000 races. Name him.
6. Which Scottish-trained horse won the Wokingham Handicap at Royal Ascot in 2008?
7. And who was the Scottish trainer?
8. Which Scot trained Double Trigger, winner of the Ascot Gold Cup in 1995?
9. He also trained the winner of the 2000 Guineas in 1994. Name this winning horse.
10. And what was significant about the 1994 victory?
11. Name the Scottish jockey who won both the Irish St Leger and Irish Oaks in the same year.
12. And name the year.
13. In which year was the Scottish Derby dropped from the racing calendar?
14. Why was the Scottish Derby dropped from the racing calendar?
15. After the Scottish Derby was reinstated in 2003, how many times was it run?
16. Who sponsored it?
17. The same trainer has won the Scottish Derby on every occasion since 2003. Name him.
18. Sir Alex Ferguson named one of his first racehorses after a street in Glasgow's Merchant City. What was its name?
19. Sir Alex Ferguson's second horse was called Queensland Star. What was the significance of the name?
20. Sir Alex Ferguson kept the Glasgow theme going with his third horse, which he bought for £200,000 in 2006. What was its name?

Scottish Horseracing: Second Division

1. In which Scottish city was Willie Carson born and brought up?
2. Which Scot came second in the Derby in 1968 on Connaught?
3. Which Irish jockey did Willie Carson lose the Championship to in 1974?
4. In which year did Willie Carson win the Oaks on the Queen's filly, Dunfermline?
5. And what made the year even more significant?
6. Who did Willie Carson replace as jockey to the Queen?
7. How many Scottish racecourses are there?
8. Name them.
9. Which company took up a three-year sponsorship deal for the Scottish Grand National in 2007?
10. How many fences are there in the Scottish Grand National – 25, 27 or 29?
11. Where is the Scottish National staged?
12. Name the famous horse which won the Scottish National and the Grand National in the same year.
13. And which year was it?
14. Name the Scottish champion trainer who broke the late Ken Oliver's record for most wins in a National Hunt season.
15. He extended the run in seasons 2002–03 with how many winners – 61, 62 or 63?
16. What distance is the Ayr Gold Cup run over?
17. Which former champion jockey rode the winner of the Ayr Gold Cup in 2009?
18. Name the champion racehorse which was part-owned by Sir Alex Ferguson before a dispute over ownership which was eventually settled out of court.
19. Which Scottish loch won the 2000 Guineas in 1983?
20. How is jockey Richard Quinn listed on racecards?

Scottish Boxing: Premier Division 1

1. In 1971, Ken Buchanan successfully defended his world title on two occasions. Name both his opponents.
2. Ken Buchanan topped the bill at Madison Square Garden in New York more than any other European boxer in history. How many times did he headline at the famous venue – 7, 8 or 9?
3. In 1975, Ken Buchanan lost in a world-title bid against which Japanese champion?
4. Name the biopic that inspired Ken Buchanan to become a boxer.
5. What was the name of the first boxing club Ken Buchanan joined in Edinburgh?
6. What was the title of Ken Buchanan's autobiography published in 2000?
7. Name the Edinburgh flyweight who, in 1928, was recognized by the New York State Commission as a world champion.
8. Who did he beat to claim the world title?
9. What was the name of Benny Lynch's trainer and manager?
10. Who did Benny Lynch beat to win the Scottish title in 1934?
11. Who did Benny Lynch lose his World Flyweight title to in 1938?
12. Under what circumstances did Benny Lynch relinquish his World Flyweight belt in 1938?
13. Name the Northern Irish fighter who Benny Lynch lost twice to, in 1936 and 37?
14. Name the fighter who knocked out Benny Lynch for the only time in his career in October 1938.
15. Name the Scottish bantamweight who lost his only world-title fight to South African Vic Toweel in 1952.
16. Name the Nigerian who foiled Jim Watt's bid to win the Commonwealth Lightweight title.
17. Why did Jim Watt withdraw from the Olympic Games in Mexico in 1968?
18. How many successful defences of his World Lightweight title did Jim Watt make – 3, 4 or 5?
19. Name the only Scots boxer to have won an Olympic gold.
20. At which Olympics did he win it?

Answers on page 221

Scottish Boxing: Premier Division 2

1. Which sport did Walter McGowan dream of pursuing before he became a boxer?
2. What was the name of Walter McGowan's father who was also a boxer?
3. What alias did Walter McGowan's father fight under?
4. Which Thai fighter did Walter McGowan lose his WBC world title to in 1966 and then fail to regain it against the following year?
5. In 1990 Pat Clinton became the first Scot to beat a fellow countryman to win the Scottish and British crowns. Who did he beat?
6. Who did Pat Clinton lose to in a European-title bid in 1989?
7. Name the Northern Irish fighter who Scott Harrison successfully defended his world title against in 2003.
8. What record did Scott Harrison set in 2004 when he knocked out Samuel Kebede at Braehead?
9. What record did Scott Harrison break in 2005 when he defeated Victor Polo?
10. Name the Scottish trainer who coached 2 of only 3 boxers to win undisputed world titles in the US.
11. The same trainer, in his fight career, won the British title and Lonsdale belt in 1959. At which weight?
12. When Alex Arthur became interim WBO Champion in 2007, what weight did he fight at?
13. How did Alex Arthur become the undisputed WBO Champion?
14. Who defeated Alex Arthur to take his title?
15. What unusual career fact does Alex Arthur share with Ken Norton, the former World Heavyweight Champion?
16. Who was the first Scottish boxer to hold the British Light-Heavyweight title when he won it in January 1960?
17. Who did Kevin Anderson beat to win the British and Commonwealth Welterweight titles in 2006 in Birmingham?
18. Anderson became only the fifth Scot to claim the British Welterweight title in 2006. Name 2 of the other 4.
19. Name the Scottish lightweight who won the British Masters title in April 2006.
20. Which Scottish boxer won the British Light-Welterweight Title when he beat Lenny Daws in January 2007?

Answers on page 222

Scottish Boxing: First Division 1

1. Who did Ken Buchanan knock out in 1968 to become British Lightweight Champion?
2. In 1970, Ken Buchanan fought unsuccessfully for the European Lightweight Title in Madrid. Who did he lose to?
3. Who did Ken Buchanan beat to win the World Lightweight title in 1970?
4. What nationality was his beaten opponent?
5. In which country did the fight take place?
6. By what means did Buchanan claim the title?
7. Out of his 69 professional fights, how many did Ken Buchanan win – 60, 61 or 62?
8. And how many of those did he win by knockout – 25, 26 or 27?
9. Name the Italian Ken Buchanan defeated to claim the European title in 1974.
10. Name the Filipino boxer who Benny Lynch outpointed to become the undisputed World Flyweight Champion in 1937.
11. At which stadium did the fight take place?
12. What age was Benny Lynch when he died – 32, 33 or 34?
13. Name the Scot who defeated Peter Kane to become the World Flyweight Champion in 1943.
14. And who did he lose his World and British Flyweight titles to in 1948?
15. Name the former Scottish boxer who retired in 1962 and went on to a successful career as a fight promoter, masterminding the career of John 'Cowboy' McCormack.
16. Who did Jim Watt beat to become World Lightweight Champion?
17. And where was his vanquished opponent from?
18. What age was Jim Watt when he won?
19. At which Scottish football stadium did Watt defend his world title against Howard Davis in 1980?
20. Who eventually took Jim Watt's world title off him in 1981?

Scottish Boxing: First Division 2

1. Who did Pat Clinton beat to win the European Flyweight title in 1990?
2. Who did Pat Clinton beat to claim the World Flyweight title in 1992?
3. How did he win?
4. Name Clinton's promoter who, when asked after the fight if the Mexican was going to be given a rematch, said: 'No. The Mexicans didn't grant a rematch at the Alamo.'
5. Who did Scott Harrison beat to claim the World Featherweight title in 2002?
6. Where was his beaten opponent from?
7. At which Scottish venue did Scott Harrison reclaim his world title in 2003?
8. What is Scott Harrison's father's name (who was also his coach)?
9. What was the name of Scott Harrison's English manager?
10. What is Scott Harrison's nickname?
11. Which manager did Alex Arthur split from in 2010?
12. Willie Limond won a world title in May 2009. Which version?
13. At which weight did he fight?
14. And who did he defeat?
15. Which Scot became WBO Light-Flyweight Champion in November 1994?
16. He had won another WBO title the previous year, can you name it?
17. Name the Scottish boxer who won the Commonwealth Featherweight title in January 2009 and successfully defended it in September 2009.
18. And which English boxer did he beat on both occasions?
19. At which Scottish football stadium did Mike Tyson fight in June 2000?
20. Tyson won in under 40 seconds. Who was his opponent?

Answers on page 223

Scottish Boxing: Second Division

1. In which Scottish city was Ken Buchanan born?
2. Name the Panamanian boxer who took Ken Buchanan's world title from him in 1972.
3. The fight ended in controversial circumstances. Why?
4. Name the Scottish Lightweight Champion Ken Buchanan fought in 1973.
5. And who won?
6. From which area of Glasgow did Benny Lynch hail from?
7. Who did Benny Lynch beat to claim the world, European and British Flyweight titles in 1935?
8. In which city did the fight take place?
9. How many times did Lynch knock his opponent down in the space of less than 2 rounds – 8, 9 or 10?
10. In which year did Jim Watt win the world title?
11. Where did the fight take place?
12. Which Scot became the World Flyweight Champion in June 1966?
13. Where in Scotland does Pat Clinton come from?
14. What was the name of Pat Clinton's dad (who was also a boxer)?
15. At which Olympics did Pat Clinton fight for Great Britain?
16. At which Scottish venue was Pat Clinton's 1992 world title win held?
17. Which sporting club is known as the 'Home of Scottish Boxing'?
18. Name the boxing promoter who owns the club.
19. Who created history in 2003 when he became the first Scottish boxer to regain a world title?
20. Which city does Scottish boxer Alex Arthur come from?

Scottish Snooker: Premier Division 1

1. Name the 3 Scottish players who have won the World Snooker Championship
2. How many times has each of them won it?
3. John Higgins was the first player to win 3 ranking events in one season as a teenager. The British and International Open were 2 of these events. What was the other?
4. In which season did John Higgins achieve this feat?
5. How many 147 maximum breaks has John Higgins compiled in his professional career – 5, 7 or 9?
6. Of his maximum breaks, John Higgins has made at least one in the World Snooker Championship. True or false?
7. John Higgins made 2 maximum breaks in 2000, both in non-ranking events. One was in the Nations Cup and the other the Irish Masters. Against which English veteran did he make his 147 at the Irish?
8. In the British Open in 1999 Graeme Dott recorded the only 147 maximum break of his career. Name his English opponent.
9. Which promising young English player did Graeme Dott overcome 9–5 in the 1995 British Open final?
10. Before winning his first ranking event at the Crucible, Graeme Dott was runner-up on 4 previous occasions in ranking events: the 1999 Scottish Open, 2001 British Open and which events in 2004 and 2005?
11. In which tournament did Graeme Dott win the second title of his career?
12. Stephen Hendry claimed his first 2 world-ranking titles during season 1987–1988 – the Grand Prix and which other tournament?
13. Which Northern Irishman did Stephen Hendry defeat 10–7 in the Grand Prix final of 1987–88?
14. How many times has Stephen Hendry won the Grand Prix – 3, 4 or 5?
15. Ronnie O'Sullivan has completed more 147 maximum breaks at the Crucible than Stephen Hendry. True or false?
16. After winning 5 consecutive Masters titles from 1989 to 1993, which fellow Scot stopped Stephen Hendry from making it 6 by beating him in the 1994 final?
17. What was the score in the final?
18. Out of the 8 ranking events in season 2008–09, how many finals did Stephen Maguire reach – 0, 2 or 3?
19. Who did Stephen Maguire lose to in the quarter-final of the 2009 World Snooker Championship?
20. Stephen Maguire won the Northern Ireland Trophy in 2007, his first ranking title in 3 years. Which Irishman did he beat in the final?

Answers on page 224

Scottish Snooker: Premier Division 2

1. Which ranking tournament did Stephen Maguire go on to win in 2008, beating Shaun Murphy in the final?
2. Stephen Maguire won his first Major title in March 2004 when he beat Jimmy White in which final?
3. Eight months later he picked up the UK Championship by beating David Gray in the final. What was the score: 10–1, 10–2 or 10–3?
4. In which year did Stephen Maguire turn professional – 1996, 97 or 98?
5. Which match was John Higgins describing when he said: 'It's my best win ever, definitely'?
6. In the 2006 Grand Prix final against Ronnie O'Sullivan, how many successive centuries did John Higgins make – 2, 4 or 6?
7. Name the Scot who made a break of 148 in 2004.
8. What was significant about it?
9. The usual route to a 147 is to pot 15 reds and 15 blacks followed by the colours in sequence. How was the 148 recorded?
10. What health condition was Graeme Dott diagnosed with in 2008?
11. Name the first Scot to make a 147 break when he cleared the table at the 1989 Scottish Professional Championships in Glasgow.
12. Name the Scot who reached 8 straight World Snooker Championship finals from 1947–54, winning twice.
13. Who did he beat in the 1947 final and then again in 1950 – Fred Davis or Joe Davis?
14. How many 147 maximum breaks has Stephen Hendry made in his career – 7, 8 or 9?
15. Stephen Hendry's maximum break total is a record but who does he share it with?
16. Which Scot beat Alan McManus in the final of the LG Cup in 2002 to claim his first major prize?
17. Name the Scot who reached the semi-final of the UK Championships in 2002 by defeating Ronnie O'Sullivan in the quarter-final
18. Which Scot reached the final of the 1996 Grand Prix – the only ranking final of his career – where he lost to Mark Williams?
19. Which Scot reached the final of the 1999 Regal China international – beating James Wattana, Ronnie O'Sullivan, Stephen Lee and Stephen Hendry en route – before losing to John Higgins in the final?
20. Which Scot reached the final of the Benson and Hedges Championship in 1995, losing to Matthew Stevens?

Scottish Snooker: First Division 1

1. Who did John Higgins beat to claim his second World Snooker Championship in 2007?
2. Why did this match go down in history?
3. Which fellow Scot did John Higgins defeat in the 2007 World Snooker Championship semi-final?
4. What unfortunate incident befell Graeme Dott at the start of the 2008–2009 season which forced him to pull out of the Shanghai Masters and the Grand Prix?
5. Who defeated Graeme Dott in the 2004 World Snooker Championship, claiming his second world title?
6. Despite losing 18–8 in the the 2004 World Snooker Championship final, what was the score in favour of Graeme Dott after the first 5 frames: 5–0, 4–1 or 3–2?
7. What age was Stephen Hendry when he won the world title in 1990 – 21, 22 or 23?
8. And what was significant about his age?
9. Stephen Hendry has lost in the World Snooker Championship final on 2 occasions, in 1997 and 2002. Who beat him in 1997?
10. And who did he lose to in 2002?
11. What was the score in the 2002 final?
12. Which bizarre incident happened during the 2006 UK Championship quarter-final between Ronnie O'Sullivan and Stephen Hendry?
13. Which former World Snooker Champion coached both Stephen Hendry and Mark Williams?
14. In 2009, who said: 'I'm only good for 2 or 3 matches a season, somehow I'm No.2 in the world but I don't know why because I'm playing like No.102'?
15. Who did John Higgins beat in the final of the Royal London Watches Grand Prix in Glasgow in 2008?
16. The tournament victory held particular significance for Higgins. Why?
17. Who beat John Higgins in the final of the China Open in 2009?
18. Who did John Higgins beat in the semi-finals at the World Snooker Championship in 2009?
19. For what bizarre reasons was the World Snooker Championship semi-final between John Higgins and Welshman Mark Williams held up in 1999?
20. Who won the match?

Answers on page 225

Scottish Snooker: First Division 2

1. Who did Stephen Hendry lose to when he recorded a maximum break of 147 in the quarter-finals of the World Snooker Championships in 2009?
2. Who did Stephen Hendry trail 14–8 in the 1992 World Snooker Championship final before coming back to win?
3. What injury did Stephen Hendry sustain after his first-round match at the 2004 World Snooker Championships which did not prevent him going on to win the tournament?
4. Which opponent said to Stephen Hendry at the 1991 UK Open: 'Hello, I'm the devil'?
5. Who did Stephen Hendry lose 17–4 to in the semi-final of the World Snooker Championship in 2004?
6. What is the furthest Graeme Dott has reached at the World Snooker Championship since winning it in 2006?
7. In an interview with *The Guardian* in 2003, which then Scottish football manager did Graeme Dott claim he would like to put in his own personal Room 101?
8. Who did Graeme Dott beat in the semi-final of the World Snooker Championship in 2006?
9. And what was the score: 17–10, 17–11 or 17–15?
10. Name the Scot who was forced to retire in 2005 with a debilitating spine condition.
11. Which Scot produced one of the most shocking results in snooker history when he whitewashed Stephen Hendry 9–0 at the 1998 UK Championship?
12. Name the 2 Scots who were at the centre of an alleged snooker match-fixing probe over their first-round match at the UK Championship in 2008.
13. Who became the first Scottish professional to reach the World Snooker Championships in 1982, where he lost his first-round match to Ray Reardon.
14. How many times did Stephen Hendry win the Scottish Masters – 2, 3 or 4?
15. Ronnie O'Sullivan won the Scottish Masters the last time it was staged, in 2002. Which Scot did he beat in the final?
16. Name the Scot who lost 3 Scottish Masters finals – in 1993, 96 and 97.
17. Which venue hosted the Scottish Masters event every year from 1990–2000?
18. At which Scottish venue was the Grand Prix held in 2006 and 07?
19. Which Glasgow venue staged the Grand Prix in 2008?
20. And in 2009, name the alternative Glasgow venue it switched to?

Answers on page 226

Scottish Snooker: Second Division

1. What is John Higgins' nickname, by which he is introduced to the audience at the start of any snooker match?
2. Which Scot is nicknamed 'the Pocket Dynamo'?
3. Who did John Higgins beat in the 1998 World Snooker Championship final?
4. What was the score in the final: 18–12, 18–13 or 18–14?
5. What impact did victory have on Higgins' ranking?
6. Who did Graeme Dott beat in the World Snooker Championship final in 2006?
7. And what was the final score: 18–12, 18–13 or 18–14?
8. What football team does Stephen Hendry support?
9. In which year did Hendry turn professional – 1985, 86 or 87?
10. Which player reached the Crucible final 6 times, failed to win it on any occasion and was beaten in 4 of these finals by Stephen Hendry?
11. Which award has Stephen Hendry won twice?
12. What is Alan McManus' nickname?
13. Who was the sponsor of the World Snooker Championship in 2010?
14. Who was the previous sponsor of the World Snooker Championship?
15. Which football team does John Higgins support?
16. In which year was Graeme Dott born – 1977, 78 or 79?
17. Name the only two Scots to have won the Grand Prix 4 times each.
18. What age did Stephen Hendry turn in January 2009?
19. Name the Scot who was nicknamed Mr Consistency for holding down a top-16 place for 16 consecutive seasons from 1990–2006.
20. What is the name of the sports management group who count Stephen Hendry and Stephen Maguire as clients?

Answers on page 226

Scottish Motorsport: Premier Division 1

1. In the 1999 CART season, Dario Franchitti finished runner-up to which ex-Formula 1 driver, then in his rookie year?
2. What award did Dario Franchitti win in 2007?
3. Name the last Scottish driver to win the Le Mans 24-hour race
4. And how many times has he won it – 1, 2 or 3 times?
5. In which year did Jim Clark die in a fatal crash?
6. In which country did Jim Clark's fatal crash happen?
7. At the 1962 Italian Grand Prix at Monza, Jim Clark was involved in a crash which killed 14 spectators and a fellow driver. Name the driver who died.
8. Which Scottish Formula One driver once said: 'If I have any legacy to leave the sport I hope it will be seen to be in the area of safety'?
9. Which Scot's website refers to him as 'the winningest British driver in US Open wheel history'?
10. In which year did David Coulthard make his Formula One debut?
11. Which driver did David Coulthard replace in the Williams team?
12. At which race did David Coulthard win his first Grand Prix in 1995?
13. David Coulthard had a brush with death in 2000 but it was not in a Formula One car. What happened?
14. In 1997, David Coulthard won 2 Grand Prix. One was in Italy, where was the other?
15. Which race has David Coulthard described as 'the crown jewel of the Formula 1 calendar'?
16. David Coulthard has won the race twice. In which years?
17. Name the Dumfriesshire village where David Coulthard comes from.
18. Which team did David Coulthard sign with in 2005?
19. At which Grand Prix in 2006 did David Coulthard record the team's first-ever podium finish?
20. And what garment did he wear on the podium?

Answers on page 227

Scottish Motorsport: Premier Division 2

1. Which fellow driver was David Coulthard referring to, after a collision at the Australian Grand Prix in 2008, when he said: 'I know I screwed up the same way with Alex Wurz) last year, and took full responsibility for it, and I would expect him to do the same. If he doesn't, I'm going to kick 3 colours of shit out of the little bastard'?
2. How many Grand Prix did David Coulthard win in his 15-year Formula One career – 10, 13 or 15?
3. How many British Rally Championships did Jimmy McRae win between 1981 and 1988 – 3, 4 or 5?
4. Which one of Jimmy McRae's rally-driving sons – Colin or Alister – won the British Rally Championship in 1995?
5. How many times did Colin McRae win the World Rally Championship (WRC)?
6. Who was the last British man prior to Colin McRae to win the World Rally Championship, in 1976?
7. How many times did Colin McRae finish runner-up in the WRC – 2, 3 or 4 times?
8. Colin McRae tragically lost his life in 2007 – how did he die?
9. Name Jackie Stewart's brother who competed in the 1953 British Grand Prix.
10. In which sport did Jackie Stewart narrowly miss out on making the British team for the 1960 Olympics?
11. What was the name of Jackie Stewart's Formula One team, in partnership with his son Paul, which competed between 1997 and 1999?
12. In 1999, they achieved their one and only victory, at the European Grand Prix. Which driver won the race for the team?
13. Ford bought the team outright in 1999. What they did name it?
14. In which Scottish town was Jackie Stewart born?
15. Name the Oban-born Scotswoman who now competes in the DTM, the German Touring Car Series.
16. Which Scot has won the Isle of Man TT on three occasions?
17. He was also first man to do a lap at what speed?
18. How many Isle of Man TT races did Scot Jimmie Guthrie win between 1930 and 37 – 5, 6 or 7?
19. Jimmie Guthrie came from which small border town?
20. How many times was Jimmie Guthrie crowned European champion – 2, 3 or 4 times?

Answers on page 227

Scottish Motorsport: Premier Division 3

1. In which country was Jimmie Guthrie killed during a Grand Prix race in 1937?
2. Name the Scottish motorcycle racer who won 11 times at the Isle of Man TT and claimed 8 podium finishes from 1985–1994.
3. He claimed a memorable victory against his long-term rival in the 1992 Isle of Man TT, which many believe to be the best TT race of all time. Who was his rival?
4. And how many times was he British Superbike champion – 1, 2 or 3 times?
5. Name the years.
6. Was he ever British 250cc Champion?
7. In which year did he die?
8. What connection did he have with Jimmie Guthrie?
9. By what name is John Crichton-Stuart better known as?
10. In which year did he win the British Formula Three Championship?
11. He raced a single season in Formula One. True or false?
12. Which famous race did he win in 1988?
13. What type of car did he win it in?
14. Can you name the 1952 founders of the Ecurie Ecosse motor-racing team?
15. In 1956 which famous race did the Ecurie Ecosse team win?
16. Can you name the Scottish drivers of the successful car?
17. What was the type of car?
18. In 1957, the Ecurie Ecosse team created a rare piece of Le Mans history. What was it?
19. The original Ecurie Ecosse team had ceased operating by 1971, but the team name was revived in the 1980s. By whom?
20. Two brothers, one of whom went to the very top of motor racing, occasionally raced for the Ecurie Ecosse team. Name them.

Answers on page 228

Scottish Motorsport: Premier Division 4

1. What is the name of the trophy received for winning the Scottish Open Speedway Championship?
2. Edinburgh Monarchs had the World Individual Speedway Champion in 1951. Can you name this champion?
3. An Edinburgh Monarch's rider won the Premier League Riders Championship in 1997. Can you name him?
4. And which Lancashire town is he from?
5. In his 981 rides for Monarchs, he accumulated the tremendous total of how many points – 1988, 2056 or 2200?
6. Edinburgh Monarchs won the Premier League twice during the last decade. In which years?
7. Name 5 of the 2010 10-man Edinburgh Monarchs team?
8. In Edinburgh Monarchs league averages, Jack Young and Peter Carr were first and second in 2010. Who was third?
9. When was speedway first introduced to Glasgow – 1928, 1933 or 38?
10. What is Glasgow's speedway team called?
11. The team have always raced in Scotland with the exception of one year. Can you name the year and the English venue?
12. Glasgow Tigers moved to their present stadium in 1999. Where is it?
13. Name 3 of the 2010 Glasgow Tigers line-up.
14. Glasgow Tigers won the Premier League in consecutive years in the 1990s. Name the years.
15. Glasgow Tigers won the Premier League Pairs Championship twice in the last decade. Name the years.
16. Glasgow Tigers moved away from their home city in 1973. Where were they based until 1977?
17. Glasgow Giants had an iconic Australian riding for them from 1949–1951 nicknamed 'the White Ghost'. What was his name?
18. The Lightening had a 4-year participation in the British League third tier from 1994, winning their league and the Knockout Cup in 1996. Where were they based?
19. Speedway came to Paisley for two years from 1975–76. What was the name of the team?
20. Where did they compete?

138 Answers on page 228

Scottish Motorsport: First Division 1

1. From which Scottish town does Indycar driver Dario Franchitti come from?
2. What series did Dario Franchitti win in 2007 and again in 2009?
3. Name the team he drove for.
4. In 2007, Dario Franchitti won a famous race. What was it?
5. Who was the first Scottish winner of the race, in 1965?
6. Which Hollywood actress is Dario Franchitti married to?
7. What is Dario Franchitti's racing driver brother called?
8. What Scottish football team does Dario Franchitti support?
9. Allan McNish and the Franchitti brothers attended a Scottish football match in 2002 as part of McNish's stag celebrations. What team did they go and see?
10. Name the Scot who was crowned Formula One Drivers World Champion in the 1960s.
11. How many times did he win it?
12. How many times did Jackie Stewart win the Formula One World Championship?
13. Which team did David Coulthard move to from Williams in 1996?
14. In the 1998 season, David Coulthard was forced to play a supporting role to which team-mate?
15. Which principality does David Coulthard call home?
16. David Coulthard never won the British Grand Prix. True or false?
17. In 2002, David Coulthard finished second in the F1 Drivers Championship. Who finished ahead of him?
18. What eating disorder did David Coulthard suffer from in his early career?
19. What is the name of the motor-racing circuit in Fife?
20. Which Scot lifted the Ladies' World Championship rally crown in 1990?

Scottish Motorsport: First Division 2

1. Name the Scot called Ireland who was born in England, lived in Wales and won the American Grand Prix.
2. Name the Scottish motorcycling legend and 3-time British Superbike Champion from 1996–98.
3. What is unique about his achievements?
4. What was Jock Taylor famous for?
5. Can you name his passenger?
6. How many Isle of Man TT successes did he achieve – 3, 4 of 5?
7. Jock Taylor lost his life in a tragic accident during a Grand Prix. In which year?
8. In which country?
9. Where is speedway team Edinburgh Monarchs' home stadium?
10. Name the 2010 Edinburgh Monarchs team captain.
11. Edinburgh Monarchs won the Scottish Cup in 2009. How many years-in-a-row have they won it?
12. Motherwell once had a speedway team. Can you name them?
13. Cowdenbeath once had a speedway team. True or false?
14. Name the 23-year-old Scot who drove the 11th-fastest time in the opening practice session at the Australian Grand Prix in 2010.
15. And who does he drive for?
16. Name his cousin, who is also a racing driver.
17. What championship did Paul di Resta win in 2006?
18. Which F1 driver did he win it from?
19. And which British F1 driver did Paul di Resta once beat to win a cadet karting championship?
20. From which part of Scotland does Paul di Resta come from?

Answers on page 229

Scottish Swimming: Premier Division

1.   What did David Wilkie wear at the 1970 Edinburgh Commonwealth Games, making him the first elite swimmer to do so in a major competition?
2.   Where did David Wilkie finish in the 200 metres breaststroke in Edinburgh?
3.   What is Wilkie's middle name?
4.   In which year did Alison Sheppard swim in her first Olympics?
5.   What age was she?
6.   Name Alison Sheppard's coach, whom she married in 1999.
7.   Alison Sheppard reached the final of the 50 metres Freestyle at the Sydney Olympics in 2000. Where did she finish?
8.   What colour of medal did Alison Sheppard win in the 50 metres Butterfly at the Manchester Commonwealth Games in 2002?
9.   Which English swimmer beat Alison Sheppard to gold in the 50 metres Freestyle at the 1998 Commonwealth Games?
10. Which Scot won a silver medal in the 100 metres Freestyle at the Tokyo Olympics in 1964?
11. Name the American prodigy who just edged him out for gold.
12. Name the Scotswoman who was the only Briton to win a swimming medal at the Olympic Games in Helsinki in 1952 when she claimed bronze in the 200 metres Breaststroke.
13. Which Scot competed in 3 Olympic Games and won silver in the 400 metres Freestyle in the Vancouver Empire Games?
14. Which Scotswoman won Britain's only swimming medal, a bronze in the 400 metres Freestyle, at the 1948 London Olympics?
15. Name the Scotsman who collected gold, silver and bronze medals on the opening day of the Scottish Gas National Championships in Glasgow in January 2010.
16. Whose bronze in the 400 metres Freestyle at the World Swimming Championships in Montreal in 2005 was the first medal in the history of the competition won by a Scottish woman?
17. Name the Scot who set a new British record in the 400 metres Freestyle at the Beijing Olympics but failed to make the final.
18. Name 2 of the 4 members of Scotland's 4 x 200 metres Medley team who won silver in Melbourne in 2006.
19. Which Scot won a bronze in the 400 metres Individual Medley in Melbourne?
20. Which Scot won a historic 3 gold medals at the European Championships, and a gold and 2 silvers at the British Empire and Commonwealth Games in 1959?

Answers on page 230

Scottish Swimming: First Division

1. Where was Scottish swimmer David Wilkie born?
2. Where did David Wilkie go to university?
3. What colour of medal did David Wilkie win in the 200 metres Breaststroke at the 1972 Munich Olympics?
4. How many gold medals did David Wilkie win at the 1974 Commonwealth Games in Christchurch?
5. Who finished second to David Wilkie in the 200 metres Breaststroke at the 1976 Olympics?
6. Who coached David Wilkie?
7. Name the Scot who held Scottish Freestyle titles between 1942 and 46 but also won Commonwealth Games gold medals for Highboard and Springboard diving in 1950, 54 and 58.
8. Which Scotswoman became Scotland's youngest-ever gold medallist when she won at the Empire Games in New Zealand in 1950?
9. Which Scotswoman won 200 metres Breaststroke silver at the Commonwealth Games in 2006?
10. What colour of medal did she win at the World Championships the following year?
11. And who beat her to gold on both occasions?
12. Name the uncle of Caitlin McClatchey who won a medal for Scotland at the 1976 Olympic Games.
13. And what colour of medal did he win?
14. David Carry won 3 medals at the Commonwealth Games in Melbourne in 2006. What colours were they?
15. Which Scottish swimmer won 2 golds at Melbourne in 2006 in the 200 metres Backstroke and 200 metres Individual Medley?
16. Name the Scottish swimmer who was named Sports Personality of the Year in 1958.
17. And what age was he at the time – 17, 19 or 21?
18. Name the Scot who won bronze in the 1500 metres Freestyle at the Atlanta Olympics in 1996.
19. What honour was Alison Sheppard awarded in 2004?
20. Which Scottish swimmer carried the Saltire into the stadium at the closing ceremony of the 2006 Commonwealth Games?

Answers on page 230

Scottish Swimming: Second Division

1. At which Olympics did David Wilkie win gold in the 200 metres Breaststroke?
2. What was significant about the time?
3. He also won a medal in the 100 metres Breaststroke at the same Games. What colour of medal did he win?
4. In 2001, which Scot finally broke David Wilkie's 25-year-old 200 metres Breaststroke record?
5. Name the Scotswoman who swam in 5 consecutive Olympics between 1988 and 2004.
6. And at which club did she learn to swim?
7. Where is Scottish Swimming's headquarters based?
8. In which country was Caitlin McClatchey born?
9. Why did she choose to compete for Scotland?
10. What is Scottish medley swimmer Hannah's second name?
11. And who is her coach?
12. Which politician described Gregor Tait as a 'national hero' after his medal-winning exploits at the 2006 Commonwealth Games?
13. At which pool in Glasgow are the Scottish National Championships traditionally held?
14. How many swimming medals did Scotland win at the 2006 Melbourne Commonwealth Games – 9, 12 or 15?
15. How many gold medals did they win – 5, 6 or 7?
16. How many gold medals did Caitlin McClatchey win at the 2006 Commonwealth Games in Melbourne?
17. And in what events?
18. Who was the last Scot to win a swimming gold in the Commonwealth Games prior to 2002?
19. Alison Sheppard was the next to win a swimming gold when she won at Manchester in 2002. What event did she win?
20. Name the Australian who coached Ian Thorpe to success and took over as head coach of British Swimming's Intensive Training Centre in December 2008.

Answers on page 231

Winter Sports: Premier Division

1. What curling title did a teenage David Murdoch win in 1995?
2. How many times has David Murdoch won the Scottish Men's Championship – 3, 4 or 5 times?
3. And how many European Championship gold medals does he have – 3, 4 or 5?
4. What Dumfriesshire village does David Murdoch come from?
5. What is David Murdoch's day job?
6. How many times has Euan Byers won the World Curling Championship – 1, 3 or 4 times?
7. Name the 21-year-old Scot who represented Britain in the Halfpipe Snowboarding at the 2010 Winter Olympics.
8. And where did he finish – 16th, 18th or 20th?
9. Which Scottish teenager reached the quarter-finals in the 500 metres Speed Skating at the 2010 Winter Olympics and was placed 11th overall?
10. What colour of medal did bobsledder Gillian Cooke win at the 2009 World Championships at Lake Placid?
11. Who is Gillian Cooke's driver in the two-women Bobsleigh?
12. What event did Gillian Cooke compete for Scotland in at the 2002 Manchester Commonwealth Games?
13. Did Gillian Cooke win a medal at the 2010 Vancouver Olympics?
14. Name the Scottish skier who finished 11th in the Men's Downhill event at the World Championships in 2005, the best result by a British man in the history of the competition.
15. And what age was he when he retired in 2009?
16. Name the Scot who is Britain's top-ranked Giant Slalom skier.
17. What is the name given to the mass outdoor curling competition staged in Scotland, which involves hundreds of rinks?
18. How many times has it been staged since 1945?
19. And name the locations.
20. And how many inches of ice does it require before it can be staged?

Answers on page 231

Other Sports

1. Which player beat Andy Murray in the final of the US Open in 2008 and the Australian Open in 2010?

Other Sports

© DC Thomson & Co. Ltd.

2.   Who is this tennis player who has represented Scotland?

Answers on page 240

© DC Thomson & Co. Ltd.

3. Name this former Scotland rugby manager.

Other Sports

4.   Who is this Scotland rugby international who earned his 100th cap in 2010?

Answers on page 240

Other Sports

5.   Name this former Scotland rugby international who was born in New Zealand.

Answers on page 240

Other Sports

6.   Who is this legendary rugby commentator who died in 2010?

Answers on page 240

© DC Thomson & Co. Ltd.

7. On how many occasions has Colin Montgomerie finished runner-up in a major championship – 3, 4 or 5 times?

Answers on page 240

Other Sports

8. Over which course did Paul Lawrie win the Open Championship in 1999?

Answers on page 240

Winter Sports: First Division

1. Which Scotswoman skipped the Great Britain Curling team to a gold medal at the 2002 Winter Olympics in Salt Lake City?
2. What was the colloquial name given to the winning stone she delivered to clinch gold?
3. Who did the GB Curling team beat in the final to win gold at the 2002 Winter Olympics?
4. Two months after that Salt Lake City triumph, Team Scotland won their first-ever World Championship gold. Who skipped them?
5. Who did Scotland lose to in the final of the Women's World Curling Championship in 2010?
6. Who skipped the Scottish team in the final of the Women's World Curling Championship in 2010?
7. And what age was she?
8. Name the woman snowboarder who competed at her third Olympics in 2010 in Vancouver.
9. Where did she finish in the Women's Halfpipe – 20th, 30th or 40th?
10. In the 2002 Olympics in Salt Lake City, who made history by becoming the first British skier to win a medal for Alpine Skiing?
11. And what colour was the medal?
12. Why was he stripped of his medal soon after?
13. And what is his nickname?
14. His brother is also an Alpine Skier. Name him.
15. Name the Scottish cross-country skier who finished 51st in the Men's 30 kilometres Pursuit at the Vancouver Olympics in 2010 and also finished just outside the top 50 in the 15 kilometres Free and the Men's Individual Sprint Classic.
16. Another Scottish teenager finished 60th in the Sprint and 74th in the 15 kilometres Free. Name him.
17. And which Aberdeenshire town do they both come from?
18. How many of David Murdoch's rink at the 2010 Vancouver Olympics were Scottish?
19. Name them.
20. What is the name of the governing body for curling in Scotland?

Answers on page 232

Scottish Cycling: Premier Division 1

1. Where did Robert Millar finish in the 1984 Tour de France?
2. And what accolade did he also win in the same race?
3. Who was Robert Millar's first trainer?
4. Where did Robert Millar finish in the Vuelta de Espana in 1985?
5. What was the name of biopic of Graeme Obree's life which was released in 2007?
6. Graeme Obree twice broke the world Hour record. In which years?
7. The first time he broke the record it lasted less than a week. Name the English rider who broke it 6 days later.
8. How many times was Graeme Obree crowned World Pursuit Champion – 2, 3 or 4 times?
9. Which domestic appliance did Graeme Obree use bearings from to build his famous, record-breaking bike?
10. What was Graeme Obree's nickname for his bike?
11. Chris Hoy won 3 gold medals at the Beijing Olympics in 2008. Who was the last Briton to win 3 golds at the Olympic Games?
12. In which events did Chris Hoy claim gold at the Beijing Olympics in 2008?
13. At the Athens Olympics in 2004, Chris Hoy won gold in an event that was discontinued for Beijing in 2008. Which event?
14. Which 1982 film by Steven Spielberg inspired Chris Hoy to cycle?
15. Before he took up track cycling, which discipline was Chris Hoy ranked 2nd in Britain and 9th in the world?
16. Chris Hoy won silver at the 2000 Olympics in which event?
17. Which breakfast cereal did Chris Hoy advertise post-Beijing 2008?
18. Which award did Chris Hoy win in December 2008?
19. Name the Formula One driver and the swimmer he finished ahead of.
20. Name the 3 Scots who won gold in the Team Sprint at the 2002 Commonwealth Games.

Answers on page 232

Scottish Cycling: Premier Division 2

1. Name the Scottish cyclist who became the fastest man to ride round the world in 2008.
2. How many full days did it take – 174, 184 or 194?
3. By how many days did he beat the previous record – 71, 81 or 91?
4. Which stage of the Tour de France did David Millar win in 2000?
5. Cyclist David Millar was banned in 2004 for taking which prohibited substance?
6. Which title did cyclist David Millar win in 2003?
7. In which country was cyclist David Millar born?
8. In which Scottish town is the UCI Mountain Bike World Cup held?
9. Which Scot won the World Junior title at the World Downhill Mountain Bike Championships in 2007?
10. What is the name of the short head-to-head race event that is staged alongside the World Downhill Mountain Bike Championship every year in Scotland?
11. Who is the manager of the Scottish Cycle Speedway team?
12. Name the Scot who won a bronze in the 20 kilometres Scratch race at the 2006 Melbourne Commonwealth Games.
13. And what is his day job?
14. Which Wick-born rider was Scottish Road Race Champion in 2005 and 2007?
15. And who was Scottish Road Race Champion in 2009?
16. Which pro team does he ride for?
17. And from which discipline did he move to road racing?
18. Which title did his family once win after appearing on a BBC series?
19. Name the Scotswoman who won a bronze medal in the Points race at the 2006 Melbourne Commonwealth Games.
20. And what was historic about the achievement?

Answers on page 233

Scottish Darts: Premier Division

1. Who was the first Scot to win the Embassy World Professional Darts Championship?
2. He won the title twice. Name the years.
3. And how many times did the same player win the British Professional Championship – 4, 5 or 6 times?
4. In August 2009 the Professional Darts Corporation (PDC) named a tournament in tribute to him. What is it called?
5. Which great rival did Jocky Wilson defeat to win the World Darts title in 1989?
6. Who was the second Scot to win the World title?
7. There were two interesting characteristics about his win. Name them.
8. Who did he defeat in the final?
9. What nickname did he use?
10. Jamie Harvey who won the Scottish Masters, Antwerp Open and reached the final of the PDC World Championship has a memorable nickname. What is it?
11. Which Scot won the BDO World Masters in 2007?
12. What was his walk-on signature tune?
13. Name the Scot who in 2007 won the World Darts Trophy, the International Darts League, the Scottish Open and British Open?
14. In 2009, he moved across to the Professional Darts Corporation and won his first tournament 3 months later. Name the tournament.
15. In 1977, Rab Smith from Dumfries defeated Eric Bristow in the final of which major tournament?
16. Which Scottish darts player was in the world top 10 during 2010, won the Welsh Open in 2009 and the British Classic in 2008?
17. Which Scottish darts player won the Belgian Open 2009, the German Open 2009 and the British Open 2008?
18. Which Scottish darts player is a cousin of Scottish footballing brothers Derek and Darren Young?
19. Which player nicknamed 'the Bear' reached the quarter-finals of the BDO World Championships in 2002–03 and won the Finnish Open in 2001?
20. Who won the Scottish Open in 2004, the Welsh Classic in 2005, the English Open in 2006 and was involved in controversy, refusing to shake hands with Mervyn King in the 2007 World Darts Championship?

Answers on page 233

Scottish Bowling: Premier Division 1

1. Which Glasgow-based club has been described as 'the Mecca of Scottish Bowling'?
2. Which Scotsman has won the World Indoor Bowls title most often?
3. How many times has he won it?
4. Name the years.
5. How many men's World Outdoor Bowls champions has Scotland had?
6. How often have Scotland won the Men's Pairs title at the World Bowls Championships?
7. How many Men's Triples titles have Scotland won at the World Championships?
8. Which Scot won the 1984 Men's World Pairs title playing for the USA?
9. Name the only Scot to have won the Champion of Champions Singles title.
10. When did Scotland last win the Commonwealth Games Men's Singles and who won it?
11. How many World Indoor Singles titles did he also win?
12. What does he do now?
13. Which Scot won the Word Indoor Singles title in 1982?
14. Hugh Duff won the World Indoor Singles title twice, 9 years apart. Name the years.
15. Bowls has been played at every Commonwealth Games since its inception in 1930 with one exception. Name the year and the country.
16. Which Men's Pair won the 2006 Commonwealth Games gold medal?
17. Which Women's Pair won the 2006 Commonwealth Games silver medal?
18. Which Men's Pair won the 2002 Commonwealth Games gold medal?
19. Who won the 1982 Commonwealth Games Singles gold medal?
20. Name the 2009 Scottish Bowls Men's Singles Champion.

Answers on page 234

Scottish Bowling: Premier Division 2

1. Which club won the 2009 Scottish Bowls Men's Pairs?
2. Which Scot was ranked No.1 for the World Bowls Tour (WBT) season 2010–11?
3. There are 4 other Scots ranked in the WBT top 20. Name them.
4. Who was the Scottish WBT No.1-ranked player for season 2009/10?
5. Which Scot won the 2010 Gravells Welsh International Open?
6. In the 2002–03 season Scots players were ranked first, second and third in the WBC. Name the players and their ranking.
7. Which Scot was the World Indoor Bowls Champion in 1983?
8. Paul Foster won the World Indoor title twice. Name the years.
9. Has David Gourley ever won the World Indoor Bowls title?
10. World rankings for the WBC began in 2001–02. Name the two Scots ranked first and second.
11. What age was bowler Richard Corsie when he made his Commonwealth Games debut in his home city of Edinburgh in 1986 – 19, 20 or 21?
12. What colour of medal did he win?
13. Bowler Richard Corsie won his first gold medal at the Commonwealth Games in Canada in 1994. Which Englishman did he beat in the final?
14. How many times did bowler Richard Corsie win the Scottish National title?
15. How many Commonwealth Games did bowler Willie Wood play in?
16. How many World Championship medals has bowler Willie Wood won – 12, 13 or 14?
17. In which year did Willie Wood first represent Scotland at bowls – 1962, 66 or 68?
18. Why did bowler Willie Wood not represent Scotland at the 1986 Commonwealth Games?
19. Bowler Willie Wood withdrew from the 2006 Games in Melbourne. Why?
20. In which year was the World Outdoor Bowls Championship last held in Scotland?

Answers on page 234

Trivia: Premier Division

1. As of May 2010, which Manchester United boss had managed the club longest, Sir Matt Busby or Sir Alex Ferguson?
2. Name the other Scot to have managed Manchester United in the last 50 years.
3. Name the three Scots to have managed Liverpool in order of longest to shortest serving.
4. Three Scots have managed Arsenal in the last 50 years. Name them.
5. Who is the only player to be voted both Scottish and English Football Writers' Player of the Year?
6. What league do Gretna now play in?
7. And what is their official name?
8. Name the Scottish manager who, when he lost his job in March 2010, had been sacked 3 times by the same club.
9. Which player did Tommy Gemmell once kick in the backside in a match against West Germany in 1969?
10. Name the 5 Scottish clubs whose names begin and end with the same letter.
11. Who scored Scotland's first-ever goal in the World Cup finals?
12. How many Celtic managers have come and gone in the space of Walter Smith's two spells in charge of Rangers?
13. Name them.
14. Name four teams who have won the Scottish League only once.
15. Name a Scotsman, two Irishman and a Welshman who have played for 3 clubs who have won the European Cup.
16. Who were the last 3 Scotland internationals to play overseas as of May 2010?
17. Name 8 current or former Celtic players whose surname ends in 'O'.
18. Which Scottish lower-division team's supporters sing, to the tune of 'When the Saints go Marching in': 'On yonder hill, there stands a coo, On yonder hill, there stands a coo, It's no there noo, It must have shiftit, On yonder hill there stands a coo'?
19. Which Scottish club, living up to its bohemian stereotype, once announced over the PA system at half-time: 'If anyone here today is willing to accommodate a German postgraduate student next semester could they please let us know'?
20. Who was the last manager in Airdrieonians' history?

Answers on page 235

Trivia: First Division

1. Which Scot won the English Player of the Year Award in 1983?
2. Which team left English football for Scottish football in 2002?
3. Which member of the Royal Family played rugby for Scottish Schools?
4. Name the Scottish coach who served under Jose Mourinho at Chelsea and then moved to West Ham as Gianfranco Zola's assistant.
5. Which Scot won the BBC Sports Personality of the Year in 1991?
6. Who became the oldest player to have appeared in a competitive match for Rangers in April 2010?
7. What age was he?
8. And whose record did he beat?
9. How many defeats did Tony Mowbray preside over in his 8-month spell at Celtic – 13, 14 or 15?
10. Who was ex-Celtic striker Henrik Larsson playing for just 8 weeks after winning the Champions League with Barcelona in 2006?
11. Which Swedish Second Division side was Henrik Larsson in charge of in 2010?
12. What season was the first of the new Scottish League Premier Division?
13. How many months did it take for FIFA to officially credit James McFadden for the goal he scored in Scotland's 2–1 win in Iceland on 10 September 2008, which was originally given to Barry Robson?
14. On 26 December 2009, which St Johnstone player ended his 16-month goal drought by scoring a hat-trick in 16 minutes against Motherwell whilst wearing the No.16 jersey?
15. Which Aberdeen footballer donated his 6-figure signing-on fee to the club's youth development operation when he made a £1 million move to Sunderland in June 2007?
16. Who had a better win ratio as Celtic manager, John Barnes or Tony Mowbray?
17. What was the name of the book that followed the fortunes of East Stirlingshire for a season?
18. Name the book in which the author travels round each of the 42 senior Scottish football grounds in the space of one season.
19. What popular Scottish football fans' website's name derives from two staples of a supporters' diet?
20. Name the son of Gordon Strachan who has a blog on the BBC website and is an aspiring journalist.

Answers on page 236

Trivia: Second Division

1. Who was Jimmy Greaves' Scottish partner on his iconic sports programme?
2. What were Livingston known as up until 1974?
3. In that year, they changed their name. What did they become?
4. What is the only club in Scotland with a 'J' in their name?
5. Name the Scottish squash player who defected to England.
6. On 12 April 1986, Dundee United were beaten 3–0 by Hearts at Tannadice. Which TV celebrity became a United fan that day after being taken to the match on a first date by the man she later married?
7. The day after Tony Mowbray was sacked by Celtic, which SPL manager said: 'When I was considering the job last year, the big attraction was the Champions League, and that's probably not going to be there ... Celtic has become a domestic job'?
8. Roy Erskine played as a full-back for Hibs reserves, Stirling Albion and Cowdenbeath in the 1950s, but who are his more famous sporting grandsons?
9. When Paul Lawrie won the Open Championship in 1999 on a much–criticized course set-up, which fellow golfer was widely quoted as saying: 'Carnoustie has got the champion it deserves'?
10. Who was the first Scot – a well-known jockey – to be a captain on the TV show *A Question of Sport*?
11. In 2009, which Scottish footballer went on Radio Scotland to sing a song he wrote called 'Sadie Burd', which begins with the lyrics: 'Sitting at home by myself, I've been left up on the shelf'?
12. What now exists where Clydebank FC's Kilbowie Park used to be?
13. Which footballer was ordered to quit indie band *The Begbies* because his then manager Eddie May felt it was affecting his performances for Falkirk?
14. On 9 November 1997, which Aberdeen player was shown 3 red cards in a match against Dundee United?
15. Which golfer represents Scotland despite having been born in Bolton in 1960 to English parents?
16. What age was Islam Feruz when he played for Celtic in the Tommy Burns tribute match on 31 May 2009?
17. Which former SPL manager said: 'My wife would like to divorce me because I told her she can go alone on the holiday as I am here to work'?
18. Which ex-Rangers full-back has played in Scotland, England, Norway, Turkey and China in the past 4 years?
19. Which footballer wrote on his Twitter page in April 2010: 'Love it when people got there roof down in glasgow and out of no where it starts raining wit the sun shining!! Shit be funny!'?
20. Glasvegas frontman James Allan was on the books of which 6 Scottish clubs?

Answers on page 236

Scottish Tennis: First Division

1. What was the name of the Barcelona tennis academy Andy Murray attended as a youngster?
2. In which year did Andy Murray win the US Open Junior title?
3. And who did he beat in the final?
4. Jamie Murray reached the Mixed Doubles semi-final at the US Open in 2007. Who partnered him then?
5. Who did Andy Murray lose to in the fourth round at the Queens tournament in 2005?
6. What physical ailment undermined him in that match?
7. And name his first and second-round opponents at that year's Wimbledon.
8. Who did he lose narrowly to in the third round in Wimbledon in 2005?
9. What height is Andy Murray?
10. Name the Scot who made his Davis Cup debut in 2006 against the Ukraine.
11. Elena Baltacha's mother Olga was also a professional athlete. In which sport did she compete?
12. What sport did her father play?
13. What round of Wimbledon did Elena Baltacha reach in 2002 – 2nd, 3rd or 4th?
14. Who did Elena Baltacha lose to in the second round of Wimbledon in 2009?
15. Which doubles pairing went by the nickname 'Booty and Stretch'?
16. How many national Scottish titles did Judy Murray win as a player – 54, 64 or 74?
17. Name the Scot who won the Australian Open Boys' Doubles title in 2007.
18. Name the Scot who coached Andy Murray in his formative years who is now the Davis Cup captain.
19. Name the Spanish veteran who coached Andy Murray from 2003 to 2005.
20. Who beat Andy Murray in the quarter-final of the 2009 French Open?

Answers on page 237

Miscellaneous Sports: Premier Division 1

1. Name the shinty player who scored eight goals in an 11–3 victory for Newtonmore over Furnace in the Camanachd Cup final of 1909.
2. Alister Allan is Scotland's most successful Commonwealth Games competitor. In which sport does he compete?
3. George Cornet won Olympic gold at the 1908 and 1912 Olympic Games in which sport?
4. How many times did Helen Elliot Hamilton win the table tennis Ladies' World Doubles Championship?
5. Name the former British and European Champion judo player who is the only British coach to have trained a double Olympic Champion, Austrian Peter Seisenbacher.
6. Name the Scottish rower who won gold at the Stockholm Olympics in 1912.
7. John McNiven competed in 6 Commonwealth Games and won 2 bronze medals in which sport?
8. Who became Scotland's first judo World Champion in 1999?
9. And what colour of medal did he win at the 2002 Commonwealth Games?
10. Equestrianist Ian Stark won 4 of the same colour of medals in 5 Olympics. Which colour?
11. How many times did Ian Stark win the Badminton Horse Trials?
12. Name the Scotswoman who reached the quarter-finals of the Wimbledon Ladies' Singles in 1970 and 71.
13. She also reached the semis of the Ladies' Doubles at Wimbledon with another Scot. Who was her partner?
14. In which year did shinty's Camanachd Association come into being – 1883, 1893 or 1903?
15. How many players are there in a shinty team?
16. Who sponsors the Camanachd Cup?
17. What is Kingussie's home ground called?
18. What colour do Kingussie play in?
19. Which shinty team won the Premier League Championship for the first time in their history in 2006?
20. And name their winning captain, who is also a professional musician.

Answers on page 237

Miscellaneous Sports: Premier Division 2

1. Why are Kingussie Shinty Club in the Guinness Book of Records?
2. Which Fort William player scored a goal after 9 seconds in the 1992 Camanachd Cup final, the fastest goal in a final?
3. Only 4 teams have won 3 successive Camanachd Cup finals. Name them.
4. How many times have Newtonmore won the Camanachd Cup – 28, 29 or 30 times?
5. Who was the Kingussie manager in 2010?
6. Name the two Scottish teams who will play in the British Elite Ice Hockey League in the 2010–11 season.
7. Name the two Edinburgh Capitals defencemen named in the 2010 British ice hockey squad.
8. Only one Edinburgh Capitals forward made the squad. Can you name him?
9. Name the Edinburgh Capitals netminder who was named in the top three of the Elite League's Netminder of the Year Award.
10. Name Edinburgh Capitals' top scorer in 2009–10 who was named in the top three of the Elite League's Newcomer of the Year Award.
11. Edinburgh Capitals' coach made the top three in the Elite League's Coach of the Year Award. Can you name him?
12. When was the Scottish Premier Ice Hockey League formed?
13. Name the 5 teams who participated in that first season.
14. The Scottish ice hockey teams are joined by 2 English teams in the Northern League. Can you name them?
15. In the 2007–08 season which team won both competitions?
16. In the league competition, what is unusual about Edinburgh Capitals' participation?
17. What historic achievement did Scottish ice hockey player Tony Hand make in 1986?
18. For which ice hockey team did Tony Hand make his senior debut at the age of 14?
19. Tony Hand became the first British ice hockey player to score how many goals?
20. Which English ice hockey team did Tony Hand go on to manage?

Answers on page 238

Miscellaneous Sports: Premier Division 3

1. In hockey, name the men's goalkeeper with 90 Scotland caps and 29 Great British caps who plays for Loughborough.
2. Which Western Wildcat midfielder has more than 150 caps?
3. He has played hockey for Surbiton, Grange, FC Barcelona and Scotland. Who is he?
4. Which women's hockey player plays defence for Olton and West Warwickshire, and has more than 150 caps?
5. Which hockey forward/midfielder who plays for Bonagrass Grove has 136 caps and 18 for Britain?
6. Name the 15-year-old who was shortlisted in the final 10 for the BBC Young Sports Personality of the Year awards in 2006.
7. Name 2 of the Scotland men's team's 4 group opponents at the 2006 Commonwealth Games in Melbourne.
8. Where did Scotland finish in the 5-team group?
9. What is the first name of the Scottish hockey international Moodie who also represented Britain at the 2004 Athens Olympics?
10. Name the Hawick-born man who was awarded the British Empire Medal for becoming the first man – along with Captain John Ridegway – to row across the Atlantic in an open boat.
11. How many days did it take him – 92, 102 or 112?
12. And what historical feat did he achieve in 1971?
13. Which Scot was one member of 'the three blondes in a boat' who won gold at the 2000 Olympics in Sydney?
14. Name the other two members.
15. Which sailing class did they win in Sydney?
16. What colour of medal did they win at the Athens Olympics 4 years later?
17. And which class?
18. At which Olympics did Scot Rodney Pattison win his first sailing gold?
19. How many Olympic medals did sailor Rodney Pattison win in total?
20. What colour of medal did Euan Burton win at the Judo World Championships in 2007?

Miscellaneous Sports: First Division 1

1. Name the Scotswoman who won Judo gold at the 2006 European Championships and silver at the Commonwealth Games in Manchester.
2. Name the Scots male judo player who represented Britain at the 2000 Olympics and won a silver medal at the 2002 Commonwealth Games?
3. Name the only dog from Scotland ever to have won the English Greyhound Derby.
4. In which decade of the 20th century did it win?
5. Who was the first British woman to be awarded an MBE in 1996 for services to shooting?
6. And how many Commonwealth Games medals does she have – 2, 3 or 4?
7. Name the Scotswoman shooter who won bronze, silver, then gold at the 1998, 2002 and 2006 Commonwealth Games respectively.
8. Who became the first Scottish woman to win 2 Commonwealth Games shooting golds in 2006?
9. And what age was she – 42, 52 or 62?
10. Name the Scottish marksman who has appeared at 7 Commonwealth Games and carried the Scottish flag at the opening ceremony in Melbourne in 2006.
11. The 53-times capped, Chinese-born badminton player Yuan Gao (formerly Yuan Wemyss) is better known by what nickname?
12. Name the Scots-born basketball player who was selected by the NBA club the Memphis Grizzlies in the 2002 draft.
13. Name the Scots gymnast who won gold in the Men's Rings at the 2002 Commonwealth Games in Manchester.
14. Name the Scots gymnast who won bronze in the High Bar at the 2006 Commonwealth Games in Melbourne.
15. The Duke of Argyll once said: 'We are ecstatic about bringing the World Cup back to Scotland.' Which sport was he referring to?
16. Who was the Scottish all-round athlete who was national champion between 1856 and 76, and excelled at everything from sprint, hurdles, tossing the caber and the hammer, to wrestling?
17. Who became the first Scot to climb Everest, in 1975?
18. Vicky Jack, from Perthshire, successfully climbed Everest in 2004. What was particularly special about her achievement?
19. Team Scotland won their seventh successive world crown at the Indoor Tug-of-War Championships in 2010. Who did the 600 kg team beat 3–0 in the final?
20. What is the name of the 7-times British Ice Dancing champions who come from Scotland?

Answers on page 239

Miscellaneous Sports: First Division 2

1. Scot Alan Pettigrew has held which world record for 25 years?
2. Name the Scot who won 6 versions of world Thai boxing and kickboxing titles.
3. Which Scot is the UK and World Dogsledding Champion?
4. Name the Scot who has held Mr Universe and Mr World titles.
5. Which Scot was twice crowned the World Highland Games Champion and has won 16 Scottish Championships?
6. And how many times was he crowned World Caber Tossing Champion – 4, 5 or 6?
7. Name the Scot who was inducted into the Scottish Sport Hall of Fame in 2002 in recognition of his amazing walking feats, which included walking 90 miles in just over 20 hours for 5,000 guineas in 1801.
8. Which Scot was deputy leader of the successful 1975 Everest Southwest Face Expedition and went on to become a world authority on mountain rescue?
9. Name the Scotswoman who won 9 medals over 3 sports – athletics, swimming and shooting – at the 1984 Paralympic Games.
10. Which women's judo player won a silver in the 57 kg Category at the 2002 Commonwealth Games?
11. Which Scots gymnast won a bronze in the Men's Vault at the 2002 Commonwealth Games?
12. Thomas Yule won a bronze medal in which sport at the 2002 Commonwealth Games?
13. Name the Scottish canoeist who won silver in the K–1 event at the 2004 Athens Olympics.
14. Name the former squash player who played for Scotland but was born in Australia.
15. And what was his highest world ranking?
16. How many Commonwealth gold medals did squash player Peter Nicol win in his illustrious career?
17. Which English player partnered him at the 2002 and 2006 Commonwealth Games in the Men's Doubles?
18. Which Canadian player did Nicol have a long rivalry with?
19. How many months was Nicol ranked world No.1 in his career – 40, 50 or 60 months?
20. Which town in Aberdeenshire is he from?

Answers on page 239

ANSWERS

Celtic: Premier Division 1

1. Dunfermline and Hibs
2. Pat Bonner
3. 37
4. True
5. Billy McNeill
6. Dunfermline
7. Willie Maley, Jock Stein and Gordon Strachan
8. Paul Lambert. The other scorers were Chris Sutton (2), Henrik Larsson (2) and Stilian Petrov (1)
9. MSV Duisburg
10. It was the first to be televised live (score was 1–1 and Clyde won the replay 1–0)
11. Bobby Lennox (the score was Celtic 1–0 Rangers after extra time)
12. William Angus
13. Tony Warner
14. Scott Marshall
15. Anton Rogan (the final score was Celtic 2–1 Dundee United)
16. Glenn Loovens
17. After Cesar Romero, the Hollywood actor who played the getaway driver in the original version of the movie *Ocean's Eleven*. McNeill was the only player to own a car at the time
18. Lemon
19. Alan McGee, the founder of Creation Records and the man who discovered the rock group *Oasis*
20. Hibs

Celtic: Premier Division 2

1. Davie Hay
2. Livingston
3. Billy Stark
4. 5–2 to Celtic
5. Manchester United
6. Bertie Auld
7. Jack McGinn
8. 2
9. Partick Thistle
10. Dion Dublin and Tommy Johnson
11. Hearts
12. Willo Flood, Juninho, Shaun Maloney and Zheng Zhi
13. Chris Sutton
14. Brother Walfrid
15. 11
16. Pat McGinlay, with 12 goals
17. Gil Heron
18. Fernando De Ornelas
19. 3 (1967, 69 and 2001)
20. Steve Guppy (Neil Lennon was the first)

Celtic: Premier Division 3

1. Dundee
2. 1903
3. Alec McNair
4. Red
5. The noise of the crowd after Jorge Cadete's debut goal
6. Willie Buchan
7. 71
8. Jimmy McGrory
9. 10
10. Brian McClair (2), Mo Johnston (2) and Paul McStay (1)
11. Johnny Doyle
12. Llanelli Town
13. Bobo Balde and Mo Camara
14. Michael Gray
15. Ujpest FC
16. Wayne Biggins
17. Martin Hayes
18. Stuart Slater
19. St Johnstone, in a 5–2 win
20. Aiden McGeady

Celtic: First Division 1

1. Jimmy McGrory with 472
2. Bobby Lennox with 273
3. Clyde in a 2–1 Scottish Cup defeat
4. Du Wei, the Chinese defender
5. Adam Virgo
6. Helenio Herrera
7. Argentinian
8. Juninho and Rafael Scheidt
9. Paolo di Canio, Jorge Cadete and Pierre van Hooijdonk
10. 22
11. Chris Sutton
12. The Cannonball Kid
13. Dentistry
14. St Johnstone, 2–0
15. Tommy Burns
16. Wim Jansen
17. Dariusz Dziekanowski
18. Steve Fulton
19. Margaret Thatcher
20. Racing Club of Argentina

Celtic: First Division 2

1. Jock Brown
2. The theme tune to *The Magnificent Seven*
3. Bobby Charlton
4. Motherwell
5. Andreas Hinkel
6. Stephen McManus
7. Enrico Annoni
8. Lyon
9. Mark Viduka
10. Pat Bonner
11. Alfredo Di Stefano (Celtic won the match 1–0 at the Bernabeu)
12. Motherwell
13. Jim Farry
14. Brian Scott
15. St Mary's Calton
16. Charlie Tully
17. Davie Hay
18. 'Big Bad John'
19. Eric Black
20. Paul and Willie McStay

Celtic: First Division 3

1. 242
2. Neil Lennon
3. 26
4. 61,000 – the exact official capacity is 60, 832
5. Demolition Derby
6. Jean-Joel Perrier Doumbe, as Celtic beat Dunfermline
7. Cameroonian
8. 23
9. Koki Mizuno
10. Garry Pendrey
11. Estadio Nacional
12. Livingston
13. NTL and Carling
14. Dr Jozef Venglos
15. Murdo MacLeod
16. 3
17. Tommy Gemmell
18. Jan Vennegoor of Hesselink
19. Lukas Zaluska
20. Diomansy Kamara (loan from Fulham) and Edson Braafheid (loan from Bayern Munich)

Celtic: Second Division 1

1. Shunsuke Nakamura
2. Jimmy Johnstone
3. Fergus McCann
4. Stevie Chalmers
5. Tommy Burns
6. Airdrie
7. Pierre van Hooijdonk
8. Brother Walfrid
9. 'The Bhoys' is their official nickname. They are also known as 'the Hoops'
10. Hoopy the Huddle Hound
11. Tony Mowbray
12. 'The Holy Goalie'
13. Kerrydale Street
14. Borussia Dortmund
15. Sean Fallon
16. John Barnes and Kenny Dalglish
17. Inverness Caledonian Thistle (3–1)
18. 'Super Caley Go Ballistic, Celtic Are Atrocious'
19. Graeme Souness
20. The Jungle

Celtic: Second Division 2

1. Paradise Windfall
2. Brian Quinn
3. Billy McNeill
4. Reggina
5. 46
6. Barrowfield
7. Paul McStay
8. 'You'll Never Walk Alone'
9. Portuguese
10. Scottish Premier League, Scottish Cup and Scottish League Cup
11. The Old Firm game
12. Dr John Reid
13. Sir Robert Kelly
14. Bill Shankly
15. Danny McGrain
16. Jock Stein
17. Peter Lawwell
18. Northern Irish
19. Middlesbrough
20. Scott Brown

Rangers: Premier Division 1

1. Ian Ferguson
2. Sweden
3. 44
4. Fiorentina
5. £5.5 million
6. Richard Gough, who signed from Tottenham Hotspur for £1.1 million in October 1987
7. 4: 2 Scottish Cups and 2 League Cups
8. William
9. 5
10. Arthur Numan, Giovanni Van Bronckhorst, Bert Konterman, Michael Mols, Frank and Ronald de Boer, Fernando Ricksen, Pieter Huistra
11. Jim Forrest in 1964–65
12. 57
13. William Wilton
14. It was adopted from an English rugby club
15. 3: the League title, the League Cup and the Scottish Cup
16. It was the first Treble in Scottish football history
17. Scot Symon
18. Andy Goram in 1989
19. 45
20. Austria

Rangers: Premier Division 2

1. 115
2. 10: League (5), Scottish Cup (2), League Cup (3)
3. 'Attila'
4. Liverpool
5. Graeme Souness
6. 28
7. £2.3 million
8. 103
9. 22
10. Middlesbrough
11. 1985
12. 28
13. 5 (which he achieved twice)
14. 'The Judge'
15. Ally McCoist, Ian Ferguson and Richard Gough
16. Ralph Brand
17. Derek Johnstone
18. David White
19. Alan Morton
20. Dunfermline and St Johnstone

Rangers: Premier Division 3

1. Filippo Maniero
2. Lawrence Marlborough
3. False. He scored 2 in the 2003–04 season
4. Rod Wallace
5. 34
6. 18
7. Jim Baxter
8. £17,500 to Raith Rovers
9. Davie White and Paul Le Guen
10. Sandy Jardine
11. 16, against Cowdenbeath in a 5–0 win in 1970
12. 14
13. Hibs, at Easter Road
14. Colin Stein, from Hibs
15. £100,000. It was the first 6-figure transfer fee between two Scottish clubs
16. Dundee
17. Johnny Hubbard. He netted 54 from 57 competitively, 23 consecutive
18. Ugo Ehiogu
19. Tugay
20. Jose-Karl Pierre-Fanfan

Rangers: First Division 1

1. Ayr United
2. 7
3. McEwan's Lager
4. Bill Struth
5. Sunderland
6. Hamilton Accies
7. Mark Hateley
8. Michael Watt
9. 7, though he gives Graeme Souness credit for the first, in the 1990–91 season
10. 2, in seasons 1991–92 and 1992–93
11. Kilmarnock
12. David Holmes
13. Norwich City
14. Jock Wallace (1972–78 and 1983–86)
15. Walter Smith (1991–98 and 2007 to the present)
16. Andy Goram
17. 2: the League and the Scottish Cup, in season 1991–92
18. PSV Eindhoven
19. Arthur Numan
20. Don Kitchenbrand and Johnny Hubbard

Rangers: First Division 2

1. Derby County
2. Ayr United
3. 4–0
4. Claudio Caniggia
5. Hearts in the 1998 Scottish Cup final. The Edinburgh side won 2–1
6. Scot Symon in November 1967
7. Rangers were top of the league and unbeaten at the time
8. 27
9. Third. Hearts were second and Celtic first
10. The Scotland national team, who were preparing for the World Cup in Argentina. Rangers won 5–0
11. Aberdeen, who finished second 5 times in 9 seasons
12. True. Two draws and a 5–1 defeat
13. 198
14. Filip Sebo
15. Bert van Lingen
16. Everton
17. Marseille
18. Bordeaux
19. Maurice Edu
20. 'The Girvan Lighthouse'

Rangers: First Division 3

1. Paul Le Guen
2. Bosnian
3. Dundee United
4. Robert Fleck
5. 3 – the League, the Scottish Cup and the CIS Cup
6. 5
7. Jock Wallace
8. Copland Road, Govan, Broomloan Road and the Bill Struth Main Stand
9. Dundee United
10. 5
11. Alfie Conn
12. Daniel Prodan
13. Monaco
14. Andy Watson
15. Jesper Christiansen
16. Gordon Durie
17. Jimmy Bell
18. False. He once played in a testimonial match but was never offered a contract
19. 'Slim'
20. None

Rangers: Second Division 1

1. Ready
2. Fleshers Haugh near Glasgow Green (1872–79)
3. 755
4. Terry Butcher
5. John Greig
6. French
7. Lyon
8. Blackburn Rovers
9. Birmingham City
10. Alex McLeish
11. 'The Little General'
12. Tore Andre Flo
13. £12.5 million
14. Slim Jim
15. Murray Park
16. 2001
17. Helicopter Sunday
18. Hibs, 1–0
19. Nacho Novo
20. Ally McCoist

Rangers: Second Division 2

1. 'The Goalie'
2. 5 ft 11 in
3. Dunfermline
4. Mikel Arteta
5. 1971
6. Edmiston Drive
7. Arsenal
8. Stefan Klos
9. Danish
10. Kenny Miller
11. Dundee
12. Spurs
13. £9 million
14. 5–1
15. Tore Andre Flo
16. Maurice Johnston
17. Alastair Johnston
18. Sir David Murray
19. Jorg Albertz
20. Kenny McDowall

Scottish National Team: Premier Division 1

1. 9 but they have only played in 8. They qualified for the 1950 World Cup in Brazil but the SFA opted not to take part as Scotland were not the British champions
2. They had withdrawn from FIFA in the 1920s
3. Andy Beattie, who took over in 1954. The team was previously picked by committee
4. He was only allowed by the SFA to take 13 players, despite the rules permitting 22
5. Dawson Walker
6. 7–0 to the South Americans
7. Austria
8. Willie Ormond
9. Matt Busby
10. He was still recovering from injuries sustained in the Munich air tragedy with Manchester United
11. Just Fontaine
12. 13
13. 9
14. 40
15. Nigeria
16. 1–1
17. Steven Thompson
18. Sweden
19. 4–1 to Sweden
20. Marcus Allback

Scottish National Team: Premier Division 2

1. Willie Ormond (1974), Ally MacLeod (1978), Jock Stein (1982, 86), Andy Roxburgh (1990), Craig Brown (1998)
2. Denmark
3. 1–0 to Denmark
4. Gordon Strachan
5. West Germany
6. Tommy Docherty
7. Belgium
8. Alex Cropley, at half–time
9. Sir Matt Busby
10. Bobby Brown
11. Denis Law, Bobby Lennox and Jim McCalliog
12. John Greig
13. Ronnie Simpson
14. 57
15. 19 in 61 games
16. Hungary. Scotland won 2–0
17. Once, in a 1–0 friendly win over Australia in March 1996
18. 14
19. Through his Glasgow-born grandfather
20. Hugh Gallacher

Scottish National Team: Premier Division 3

1. Lawrie Reilly
2. 11–0, over Ireland in 1901
3. 7–0 defeat to defending world champions Uruguay during the 1954 World Cup finals in Switzerland
4. George Young, 48 times in 53 appearances
5. Frank McGarvey
6. Willie Johnston
7. Jim Cruickshank
8. Andy Gray, who moved from Aston Villa to Wolves in 1979 for a then British record £1.5 million
9. John Hewie
10. Bobby Clark
11. 1
12. Ian Ure
13. Vera Pauw
14. Pauline Hamill
15. Denis Law
16. Peter Lorimer and Joe Jordan
17. West Germany
18. Ibrox and Pittodrie
19. 'Ole Ola'
20. Rod Stewart

Scottish National Team: Premier Division 4

1. 'Say it with Pride'
2. Umbro
3. Diabetes
4. Estonia, in a 2–0 win for Scotland in March 1997
5. The Faroe Islands, in a 3–1 win in September 2003
6. Rab Douglas
7. Luis Figo
8. Lee Wilkie
9. Robbie Stockdale
10. Austria
11. Christian Panucci
12. Luca Toni
13. Roberto Donadoni
14. Craig Beattie
15. 9
16. Stuart McCall
17. Iceland
18. Aberdeen
19. USA
20. True. He won 2 caps in the early 1970s

Scottish National Team: Premier Division 5

1. 26
2. Georgia
3. Claret/Red
4. Klaus Toppmoller
5. Czech Republic
6. Ibrox
7. John McGinlay
8. Joachim Bjorklund, Henrik Larsson and Jonas Thern
9. John Wark
10. *So I Married an Axe Murderer*
11. Croatia
12. Kenny Miller
13. 3
14. Macedonia and Iceland twice
15. None
16. 0–0
17. The original fixture, in Tallinn on 9 October, was called off after just 3 seconds. The Estonian team failed to turn up when FIFA demanded a daylight kick-off following Scottish protests about the floodlights. Monaco was settled on as an alternative venue
18. 16
19. Philippe Troussier
20. False. The game finished 2–1 but it was played at Celtic Park

Scotland National Team: First Division 1

1. 1974
2. Willie Ormond.
3. They beat Zaire by fewer goals than Brazil and Yugoslavia had, so were eliminated on goal difference
4. 0–0
5. Gary McAllister
6. Alan Shearer
7. Ally McCoist
8. Patrick Kluivert
9. David Taylor, the then SFA chief executive, when announcing Berti Vogts' appointment
10. 7
11. Peru
12. Don Masson
13. 3–2 to Scotland
14. Archie Gemmill
15. Kenny Dalglish
16. Johnny Rep
17. Willie Johnston
18. Joe Jordan. Against Zaire in 1974, Peru in 1978 and the USSR in 1982
19. 'Easy Easy'
20. Number 20

Scotland National Team: First Division 2

1. Jim Leighton
2. 91
3. 2
4. Sweden (1992) and England (1996)
5. Queens Park
6. True. McLeish has 77 caps, one more than McStay
7. New Zealand
8. Zico, Oscar, Eder, Falcao
9. 2–2
10. Czechoslovakia, 2–1 in September 1973
11. Joe Jordan
12. Frank and Eddie Gray, who played for Leeds United
13. Eddie with 32. Frank earned 12 caps
14. Graeme Souness
15. 1872
16. West of Scotland Cricket Club's ground at Hamilton Crescent in Partick, Glasgow
17. 0–0
18. The Wembley Wizards
19. Alex Jackson
20. Mo Johnston
21. Ray Houghton, who was born in Glasgow but played for the Republic of Ireland. He scored against Italy

Scotland National Team: First Division 3

1. Brazil
2. Muller
3. Rose Reilly
4. John Robertson
5. John White
6. He was struck by lightning
7. Norway
8. Christian Dailly
9. False. He has 2 caps
10. Craig Burley
11. 3–0
12. Craig Burley
13. Alan McInally (Bayern Munich) and Murdo MacLeod (Borussia Dortmund)
14. Denis Law (Torino), Joe Jordan (AC Milan and Verona) and Graeme Souness (Sampdoria)
15. Iceland in 2002
16. Craig Burley, Paul Lambert, Brian Martin, Stevie Crawford, Scot Gemmill
17. Andrew Watson in 1881
18. British Guyana
19. Nigel Quashie in 2004
20. Walking his dog

Scotland National Team: First Division 4

1. Colin Hendry
2. John Greig
3. Jim Baxter
4. Pele
5. Graeme Souness
6. Tommy Docherty
7. Ernie Walker, then secretary of the SFA
8. Franck Ribery
9. Neville Southall
10. Ian Rush and Mark Hughes
11. Gordon Strachan
12. 9
13. False. He won one cap in a friendly against Poland in April 2001
14. 58
15. Galashiels
16. True
17. False, he won 1 cap
18. Dennis Bergkamp
19. Paul McStay, Brian McClair and Gary McAllister
20. Ronnie Simpson

Scotland National Team: First Division 5

1. Villa Park, home of Aston Villa
2. Tommy Gemmell
3. David Clarkson
4. Scotland lost 3–1
5. Australia
6. 2–0 on aggregate
7. Alex Ferguson, who took over following the death of Jock Stein the previous year
8. Walter Smith
9. Andy Roxburgh – qualified for Italia 90 World Cup and Euro 92 in Sweden
10. True
11. Michael Oliver
12. James Morrison
13. 5–0
14. Jorge Cadete
15. 2–2
16. John Petersen
17. Teacher
18. Paul Lambert and Barry Ferguson
19. Scott Dobie
20. Spain, Czech Republic, Lithuania, Liechtenstein

Scotland National Team: Second Division 1

1. Saudi Arabia
2. Craig Brown
3. Don Hutchison
4. Brazil
5. John Collins
6. Tom Boyd
7. Hampden Park
8. Kenny Dalglish
9. 102
10. Ally MacLeod
11. Scotland manager Jock Stein collapsed and died
12. Boozegate
13. Denis Law and Kenny Dalglish
14. 30
15. Jimmy Hill
16. Costa Rica
17. Andy Roxburgh
18. Diego Maradona
19. Neil Sullivan
20. John Wark

Scotland National Team: Second Division 2

1. 19
2. South Africa
3. Italy
4. 2–0: Andrea Pirlo scored twice
5. Gordon Smith
6. David Taylor
7. Jim Farry
8. 'Flower of Scotland'
9. David Taylor, then SFA chief executive
10. John Kennedy
11. James McFadden
12. Graeme Souness
13. Gary Caldwell
14. Paul Hartley
15. Queen's Park
16. Anna Signeul
17. Swedish
18. Navy blue
19. A lion rampant
20. George Peat

Scotland National Team: Second Division 3

1. Billy Stark
2. Rainer Bonhof
3. Tommy Burns
4. German
5. Tommy Burns and Ally McCoist
6. Mount Florida
7. The Hampden Roar
8. True. It takes its name from Charles Hampden, a 17th-century English parliamentarian
9. Faddy
10. True
11. Red
12. Duncan Ferguson
13. The Tartan Army
14. 'Scotland the Brave'
15. Barry Ferguson
16. John Gordon Sinclair
17. 'Big Jim Holton's after you'
18. Six foot one
19. Scot
20. Allan McGregor

Scotland National Team: Second Division 4

1. 'When will we see your likes again?'
2. 'I'm Gonna Be (500 miles)'
3. Lesser Hampden
4. Frank Haffey
5. Jim Baxter
6. Julie Fleeting
7. Willie Miller and Alan Hansen
8. Terry Butcher
9. Chris Iwelumo
10. Kris Boyd
11. Diego Maradona
12. 1–0 to Argentina
13. Celtic Park
14. Kris Boyd, James McFadden, Kenny Miller, Darren Fletcher
15. The Caldwell brothers, Gary and Steven
16. Gary
17. Jimmy Johnstone
18. *Trainspotting*
19. See You Jimmy hat
20. Barry Ferguson

Scotland National Team: Second Division 5

1. True
2. Holland
3. 6–0
4. Ruud Van Nistelrooy
5. Craig Brown
6. World Cup 1998
7. France
8. 'Ally's Tartan Army'
9. Chelsea
10. Derby County
11. He was stuck in snow at his Fife home
12. Peter Houston
13. Czech Republic, 1–0, in March 2010
14. Scott Brown
15. Adidas
16. Darren Fletcher
17. Barry Ferguson
18. 50
19. Ronnie Browne
20. Andrew Driver

Scottish Clubs in Europe: Premier Division 1

1. Mark Burchill in 3 minutes in a 7–0 win against Jeunesse Esch
2. Valencia
3. Bobby Carroll
4. 4–0 to MTK Budapest
5. George Connelly
6. Joos Valgaeren. He missed from 12 yards twice after the referee ordered his first kick to be retaken
7. Rafael Benitez
8. Nicola Amoruso
9. Joos Valgaeren
10. 3–0
11. Kenny Miller and Stephen Pearson
12. Gary Caldwell
13. Scott McDonald
14. 5–1 to Arsenal
15. Wolves
16. 3–1 to Rangers on aggregate
17. Ralph Brand (1) and Alex Scott (2)
18. Abdoulay Konko, Adriano, Luis Fabiano, Freddi Kanoute
19. It was a Ricardo Gomes own goal
20. Romania

Scottish Clubs in Europe: Premier Division 2

1. Bayern Munich
2. 3–1
3. Max Murray, beating Nice 2–1 in a European Cup match
4. Four times – once against Panathanikos and Sporting Lisbon and twice against Fiorentina
5. Nacho Novo
6. Kirk Broadfoot, Carlos Cuellar, Sasa Papac, Steven Davis and Brahim Hemdani
7. It was the competition's inaugural season, having superseded the old European Cup
8. Club Brugge, Marseille and CSKA Moscow
9. 2–2 against Marseille
10. Gary McSwegan
11. Mark Hateley
12. CSKA Moscow
13. Scott Nisbet
14. Bayern Munich, Galatasaray and Sturm Graz
15. Parma
16. Tony Vidmar and Claudio Reyna
17. Fabio Cannavaro
18. Linas Pilibaitis after 87 minutes
19. Kevin Thompson
20. Graeme Souness (Liverpool), Basile Boli (Marseille), Frank and Ronald de Boer (Ajax), Stefan Klos (Borussia Dortmund), Henning Berg (Man United), Giovanni van Bronckhorst (Barcelona), Rino Gatusso (AC Milan)

Scottish Clubs in Europe: Premier Division 3

1. Aberdeen (Cup Winners' Cup and European Super Cup)
2. Csaba Laszlo
3. Murrayfield
4. David Narey in 1977
5. 1984
6. AS Roma
7. Jock Stein
8. 4–0 to Valencia
9. Via a playoff, which Valencia won 1–0
10. FC Sion of Switzerland
11. Karl-Heinz Rummenigge and Hans Pflugler
12. Porto, 2–0 on aggregate
13. Scott Booth
14. Borussia Dortmund, versus Cruzeiro, in 1997
15. UEFA Cup first round, 1981, versus Ipswich. Aberdeen won 4–2 on aggregate
16. Billy Dodds (2), Stephen Glass (1) and Duncan Shearer (1)
17. 3–1 to Zalgiris Vilnius
18. Bohemians
19. They were the first Scottish team to be knocked out of a European competition by an Irish team
20. Ebbe Skovdahl

Scottish Clubs in Europe: Premier Division 4

1. 9
2. Bob Shankly
3. AC Milan
4. Kilmarnock, who recovered from a 4–0 deficit to beat Eintracht Frankfurt 5–4 on aggregate in the Inter-Cities Fairs Cup
5. Tommy McLean
6. Hibernian
7. 1956
8. The semi-final, where they were beaten by French side Reims
9. Pat Stanton
10. 1989
11. Videoton of Hungary
12. Andy Goram
13. FC Liege
14. Rosenborg
15. Juventus
16. FC Nordsjaelland, 4–2 on aggregate
17. Denmark
18. Morten Weighorst
19. Airdrie United's Excelsior Stadium
20. Bob Harris

Scottish Clubs in Europe: First Division 1

1. FK Suduva
2. Garry Flitcroft
3. John Hartson
4. Gerard Houllier
5. Henrik Larsson
6. Paul Lambert
7. Nuno Capucho
8. Derlei
9. Villarreal
10. Juan Roman Riquelme
11. Harald Brattbakk
12. Paddy McCourt
13. True
14. John Hartson
15. Magnus Hedman
16. Massimo Donati
17. Jiri Jarosik
18. Dinamo Batumi
19. Paris Saint Germain
20. Patrice Loko

Scottish Clubs in Europe: First Division 2

1. Real Madrid
2. George McCluskey and Johnny Doyle
3. Billy McNeill
4. Xavi Hernandez
5. Bordeaux
6. Marc-Antoine Fortune
7. Parma
8. Sergio Porrini
9. Lorenzo Amoruso
10. Gary McAllister scored after 64 seconds in the first leg at Ibrox. Eric Cantona scored in the second leg
11. John Lukic. It was an own goal from a corner
12. Ian Durrant
13. Ally McCoist
14. Mark Hateley and Ally McCoist
15. Jean Claude Darcheville and Steven Whittaker
16. Fiorentina
17. Ralph Brand, with 5 goals
18. Bayern Munich
19. Alex McLeish
20. John Hewitt

Scottish Clubs in Europe: First Division 3

1. Five: Willie Miller, Alex McLeish, Gordon Strachan, Eric Black and Mark McGhee
2. Josh Walker and Sone Aluko
3. Steve Lovell (83 minutes)
4. Lucio, Daniel Van Buyten, Mark Van Bommel, Lukas Poldoski
5. Czech Republic
6. 8 −1 to the Czechs
7. Charlie Mulgrew in the first leg
8. Barry Town (Wales)
9. 1987
10. Terry Venables
11. Elfsborg
12. Doug Somner
13. St Etienne
14. Ruud Gullit
15. Johan Cryuff
16. Frank McGarvey
17. Brian Gallagher
18. Hammarby
19. Tromso
20. Mechelen

Scottish Clubs in Europe: First Division 4

1. Ebbe Skovdahl
2. Katowice
3. Real Madrid beat them 7–3 on aggregate
4. Shelbourne
5. Jim McIntyre
6. Nice
7. Sturm Graz
8. Barry Wilson
9. MyPa 47
10. Perugia
11. Nacho Novo
12. 8–1 to Dundee
13. Alan Gilzean
14. Sporting Lisbon
15. 4–2 to Dundee
16. Anderlecht
17. 4–1 to Dundee
18. Alan Cousin and Gordon Smith
19. 5–2 on aggregate
20. Wembley Stadium

Scottish Clubs in Europe: Second Division 1

1. Artmedia Bratislava
2. Real Madrid
3. Alex Ferguson
4. Alfredo di Stefano
5. John Hewitt
6. Dick Advocaat
7. The City of Manchester Stadium
8. Neil Alexander
9. Rangers 0–2 Zenit St Petersburg
10. 7–3
11. Bayern Munich defeated them 4–1 on aggregate
12. Easter Road
13. Jimmy Nicholl
14. They were the first Scottish club to reach that stage
15. Inter Milan
16. Peter Lovenkrands
17. Villarreal
18. 3–3. Villarreal progressed on away goals after a 2–2 draw at Ibrox
19. Peter Lovenkrands
20. UnireaUrziceni

Scottish Clubs in Europe: Second Division 2

1. Vaduz
2. Eddie May
3. Vaduz, 2–1 on aggregate
4. Ryan Flynn
5. 1972
6. Dynamo Moscow
7. Barcelona
8. The Barca Bears
9. Jose Mourinho
10. Martin O'Neill
11. Henrik Larsson
12. Both headers
13. Bobo Balde
14. 1987
15. Jim McLean
16. Gothenburg
17. 2–1 to Gothenburg
18. The Lisbon Lions
19. Inter Milan
20. Jock Stein

Scottish Clubs in Europe: Second Division 3

1. Stevie Chalmers
2. Billy McNeill
3. Bayern Munich
4. Scot Symon
5. Fiorentina
6. 4–1 to Fiorentina
7. They became the first British team to reach a major European final
8. Shunsuke Nakamura
9. Louis Saha
10. Jan Vennegoor of Hesselink
11. 1–1
12. Scott McDonald
13. Spartak Moscow
14. Lionel Messi of Barcelona
15. Lyon
16. Dnipro Dnipropetrovsk
17. Dnipro won 5–1
18. Ukraine
19. Tony Mowbray
20. Mark McGhee

General Football Knowledge: Premier Division 1

1. Lazio
2. Thomas Berthold
3. Jorge Burruchaga
4. Auxerre
5. German international Lukas Podolski
6. Gerd Muller
7. 10
8. False. They reached the 1958 World Cup finals. They were beaten at the quarter-final stage by Brazil
9. Blackburn Rovers
10. Grantham Town
11. Christian Gross
12. England goalie David James
13. George Best in 2000
14. Bill Nicholson
15. Emile Heskey
16. Oleg Salenko (Russia) and Hristo Stoichkov (Bulgaria)
17. Davor Suker
18. 600 (actual number was 606)
19. 3
20. Bobby Moore, Jack Charlton and Martin Peters

General Football Knowledge: Premier Division 2

1. 108
2. Santos (Brazil)
3. 1957
4. 1867
5. 1904
6. Stanley Matthews
7. Gary Charles
8. 3
9. Alf Common
10. Denilson
11. £46 million
12. Viv Anderson
13. Johnny Haynes of Fulham, in 1961
14. Brian Deane of Sheffield United
15. Peter Withe
16. Sampdoria
17. Ronald Koeman
18. Wembley Stadium
19. Basile Boli
20. Karl-Heinz Reidle

General Football Knowledge: Premier Division 3

1. Brazil
2. Real Madrid's Bernabeu Stadium
3. Otto Rehhagel
4. Angelos Charisteas
5. Portugal
6. Poland and the Ukraine
7. Yasuhiko Okudera
8. Germany, for FC Koln
9. Parma
10. Philippe Troussier
11. Turkey
12. Zlatan Ibrahimovic
13. Jose Mourinho
14. He suffered a snapped Achilles tendon
15. Johan Mjallby
16. Paul Le Guen
17. Celtic
18. Preston North End
19. Strasbourg
20. Nancy

General Football Knowledge: First Division 1

1. Garrincha
2. Uruguay
3. Trevor Francis (Birmingham to Nottingham Forest)
4. A broken neck
5. Peter Shilton (125 caps)
6. 5 (as of May 2010)
7. Real Madrid, 9 times
8. Edson Arantes do Nascimento
9. Bruce Rioch
10. Mathieson
11. Bob Paisley
12. £440,000
13. It was a British record at the time
14. Madeira
15. Sporting Lisbon
16. Preston North End
17. Neil Sullivan
18. Roberto Baggio
19. Sweden
20. Ron Atkinson

General Football Knowledge: First Division 2

1. Bill Shankly
2. Jose Mourinho
3. Brian Clough
4. Claudio Ranieri
5. Monaco
6. Mario Kempes
7. They failed to qualify
8. While sniffing an old newspaper under a hedge, it uncovered the Jules Rimet trophy, which had been stolen in the build-up to the tournament
9. 'The Magical Magyars'
10. David Healy
11. He became manager of Dutch side FC Twente
12. 1958
13. 1992–93
14. Don Revie, the Leeds manager
15. Sir Alex Ferguson
16. 49
17. Neville Neville
18. Sheffield Wednesday
19. George Weah
20. Marc-Vivien Foe

General Football Knowledge: First Division 3

1. Emilio Butragueno
2. Burnden Park
3. Miroslav Klose
4. Carlos Alberto
5. Kevin Keegan
6. Kevin Keegan
7. Mark Hughes
8. Benfica
9. Manchester City
10. West Ham
11. Arsenal's Thierry Henry, after Larsson had come on to change the game for Barcelona in the 2006 Champions League final
12. Turin
13. James Milner
14. Randy Lerner
15. Lyon
16. Wolves
17. Birmingham City
18. Norwich City
19. The Britannia Stadium
20. Samuel Eto'o and Lionel Messi
21. Mike Phelan

General Football Knowledge: Second Division 1

1. 17
2. Eusebio
3. Glasgow
4. Jose Mourinho
5. Alan Hansen
6. Brazil
7. Zizou
8. Italian defender Marco Materazzi
9. George Best
10. Sir Alex Ferguson after his Manchester United team won the 1999 Champions League final
11. Brian Clough
12. Diego Maradona
13. The Hand of God
14. Liverpool
15. Arsenal and Spurs
16. Argentina
17. Kenneth Wolstenholme, just as Geoff Hurst scored to seal England's 1966 World Cup final victory
18. Brazil
19. Roman Abramovich
20. Thierry Henry

General Football Knowledge: Second Division 2

1. Hearts and Hibs
2. Everton
3. Steve McClaren
4. Eric Cantona
5. Highbury
6. Burnley
7. Bill Shankly
8. Melchester Rovers
9. 7–3 to Real Madrid
10. Hampden Park, Glasgow
11. Alf Ramsey
12. 2007
13. Raith Rovers
14. Anton
15. Bobby Moore
16. Bayern Munich
17. Ole Gunnar Solksjaer
18. Real Madrid and Barcelona
19. Stamford Bridge
20. Argentina

HEARTS and Hibs: Premier Division 1

1. Kilmarnock won the league with a superior goal average of 0.04%. Goal average was replaced by goal difference the following season. Hearts would have won the league on goal difference
2. Dave Mackay
3. Clyde
4. Twice, 1958 and 1960
5. 3
6. 27 goals in 38 appearances
7. 2
8. As the 'Walker final' for Bobby Walker's influential role in the 4–3 victory over Celtic
9. Stephane Paille
10. John Robertson in season 1989–90
11. 17
12. Jimmy Murray
13. 1963
14. 1976–77
15. John Hagart
16. Willie Ormond
17. Eamonn Bannon
18. Alex MacDonald
19. Cowdenbeath
20. True. He made a guest appearance in a Hearts shirt in a testimonial match for Alex MacDonald against Rangers in 1983

HEARTS and Hibs: Premier Division 2

1. It takes its name from the Old Tolbooth of Edinburgh which stood on the Royal Mile, adjacent to St Giles
2. Tom Purdie
3. Roald Jensen
4. Norwegian
5. Rene Moller
6. Wolverhampton Wanderers
7. 3–2 to Hearts
8. Donald Ford
9. Czech
10. 17
11. Takis Fyssas
12. Graham Rix
13. 4 months
14. Andy Webster
15. Wigan Athletic
16. Hibs, in a 2–1 defeat in April 1998
17. Alan 'Nipper' Lawrence, from Airdrie
18. St Johnstone
19. 1–0 to St Johnstone
20. Pasquale Bruno

1. Andy Goram (cricket), Oli Gottskalksson (basketball) and William Harper (boxing)
2. Joe Tortolano
3. The club first moved to the Easter Road area in 1880
4. Mixu Paatalainen
5. Hibs 6–2 Hearts
6. True
7. 16
8. Neil Martin
9. It is the Roman name for Ireland. The club was founded by Irish-born football enthusiasts
10. Alan Rough
11. He moved to Nottingham Forest in an £80,000 deal
12. Rangers. Thomson's was the winning goal in a 2–1 victory
13. Dundee United
14. Norwich City
15. 1973
16. Hibs' biggest win over city rivals Hearts, 7–0, which took place in 1973
17. Jock Stein
18. Finland in 1965
19. 4
20. The Famous Five Stand

1. Gordon Smith, Willie Hamilton, Alan Gordon, Peter Marinello, Darren Jackson, Paul Hartley, Michael Stewart
2. Dundee
3. Willie Bauld
4. 1906, the Scottish Cup
5. Tommy Walker
6. Craig Gordon, at 24
7. Rangers
8. 5–1
9. John Colquhoun
10. False. He appeared 3 times
11. Newcastle United
12. £750,000
13. 271
14. 27
15. 1874
16. True
17. Billy Brown
18. Edgaras Jankauskas
19. Leicester
20. John Robertson
21. Uganda

Hearts and HIBS: First Division 2

1. Colin Stein
2. It was the first 6-figure transfer between two Scottish clubs
3. Eduardo Hurtado
4. Sir Tom Farmer CBE
5. The Skol (League) Cup
6. Alex Miller
7. Dunfermline
8. Tommy McIntyre
9. Keith Wright. The game finished 2–0 to Hibs
10. Hearts, in a 1–1 draw
11. Franck Sauzee
12. 23
13. 3
14. Jock Stein
15. Bob Shankly
16. Real Madrid
17. Peter Cormack and Pat Quinn
18. 33
19. True
20. Partick Thistle, at Easter Road

Hearts and HIBS: First Division 3

1. 21,000
2. 1997–98
3. 23
4. Alex McLeish
5. Hibs lost 3–0 to Celtic
6. Ivan Sproule
7. Kilmarnock
8. Abdessalam Benjelloun and Steven Fletcher
9. Rob Jones
10. Alex Miller
11. Alen Orman
12. 17
13. 'Broony'
14. Arsenal
15. Steven Tweed
16. Joe Harper
17. Celtic
18. 6–3
19. Joe Baker
20. He was the first Englishman to achieve it.

HEARTS and Hibs: Second Division 1

1. Gary
2. Tynecastle Stadium
3. Gorgie
4. Rangers
5. Stephane Adam
6. Jim Jefferies
7. Celtic Park
8. Gilles Rousset
9. Maroon
10. Hibernian
11. Gretna, after extra time and penalties
12. The Second Division
13. Valdas Ivanauskas
14. Paul Hartley
15. Vladimir Romanov
16. George Burley
17. George Foulkes
18. Craig Gordon
19. True. He was at Hearts from 1946 until 1962
20. Craig Levein

HEARTS and Hibs: Second Division 2

1. Sunderland
2. £9 million broke the British transfer record for a goalkeeper
3. Craig Gordon, Steven Pressley and Paul Hartley
4. Hartley and Pressley both joined Celtic
5. Jimmy Wardhaugh, Willie Bauld and Alfie Conn
6. Gary Mackay
7. True. He almost signed for the Easter Road side as a young player
8. Wallace Mercer
9. 'The Jambos' but they are sometimes referred to as 'the Jam Tarts'
10. Willie Bauld
11. Raith Rovers
12. Roman Romanov
13. Vladimir Romanov
14. Christian Nade
15. Graham Weir. The game ended 4–4
16. Steven Pressley
17. 4–0
18. Paul Hartley
19. Mirsad Beslija
20. Bosnian

Hearts and HIBS: Second Division 3

1. Easter Road
2. Leith
3. 'The Hibees'
4. The Proclaimers
5. 'Sunshine on Leith'
6. 'Budgie'
7. Franck Sauzee
8. Rod Petrie
9. Lokomotiv Moscow
10. £1.6 million
11. True
12. Gordon Smith, Bobby Johnstone, Lawrie Reilly, Eddie Turnbull and Willie Ormond
13. 3: 1948, 51 and 52
14. Willie McCartney
15. Russell Latapy
16. Tony Mowbray
17. Hands Off Hibs
18. Morton
19. John Collins
20. Burnley

Hearts and HIBS: Second Division 4

1. Willie McKay
2. £2 million
3. Celtic
4. £4.4 million
5. It was the biggest-ever paid between two Scottish clubs
6. Rangers
7. Livingston
8. 2–0 to Livingston
9. Irvine Welsh
10. Peter Marinello
11. Arsenal
12. £100,000
13. 'Turnbull's Tornadoes'
14. 69
15. Gerry McCabe
16. True
17. A postman
18. Alex McLeish
19. Gareth Evans
20. Jamie McCluskey

North of the Tay: Premier Division 1

1. Aberdeen, Orion and Victoria United
2. Jimmy Philip
3. Black and gold
4. 1947, the Scottish Cup
5. 1954–55
6. Martin Buchan
7. Manchester United paid £125,000 for him
8. 89
9. 5
10. Chris Anderson
11. Willie Lennie against Wales at Dens Park
12. St Mirren
13. Tommy Craig
14. Derek McKay
15. Cup Tie McKay
16. Joe Harper
17. Doug Rougvie
18. Peter Weir
19. Paul Mason
20. Thomas Solberg

North of the Tay: Premier Division 2

1. 1960s
2. Jim McIntyre
3. Scott Paterson
4. 10 months
5. 8
6. Danish
7. Garry Kenneth
8. 108
9. 6
10. None
11. Brann Bergen
12. 4
13. 3
14. 2–1 to United
15. Platense
16. Doug Smith
17. Electrical engineering
18. Dave Bowman
19. Paul Gallacher
20. Michael Marra

North of the Tay: Premier Division 3

1. Billy Steel
2. George Anderson
3. Alfie Boyd
4. Our Boys and East End
5. 1910
6. Billy Kirkwood
7. 9
8. Barry Smith
9. Tam McManus
10. Raith, 1–1
11. Eddie Annand
12. Lee Mair's proposed move to Dens. Duffy felt Mair and his agent had used Dundee's offer of a contract to lever a better deal with Dundee United
13. Simon Lynch
14. Davie Farrell
15. Jan Zemlik
16. Kevin McDonald
17. Ron Dixon
18. They installed various facilities in a disastrous attempt to bring back greyhound racing at Dens Park
19. Tommy Coyne with 37 goals
20. Dave Smith, from Plymouth Argyle

North of the Tay: First Division 1

1. Bobby Clark
2. Brian Irvine
3. Ian Porterfield
4. Duncan Shearer
5. Gordon Strachan
6. Billy McNeill
7. 'Bumper'
8. Billy Stark
9. Scott Booth
10. Zoltan Varga
11. *The Don: The Willie Miller Story*
12. Dundee
13. Duncan Shearer and Billy Dodds
14. Hicham Zerouali
15. Robbie Winters
16. 41
17. Raith Rovers
18. Gary McDonald
19. Queen's Park
20. Firhill

North of the Tay: First Division 2

1. Jerry Kerr
2. Partick Thistle
3. Owen Coyle
4. Falkirk
5. 5–1 to Falkirk
6. Bristol City
7. Christian Dailly
8. Billy Dodds
9. Derek McInnes
10. Paul Sturrock
11. 1979, the League Cup
12. Aberdeen, 3–0 after a replay
13. Dundee
14. Dens Park
15. Chelsea for a fee of £165,000
16. Hamish McAlpine
17. Former Dundee United goalkeeper Grzegorz Szamotulski
18. Cowdenbeath
19. Paul Dixon
20. He was signed as a striker and later moved to central defence

North of the Tay: First Division 3

1. 1893
2. 52
3. Spurs
4. £72,500
5. Gordon Wallace
6. Tommy Gemmell
7. Leigh Griffiths
8. Livingston
9. Juan Sara
10. Gavin Rae
11. He was diagnosed with multiple sclerosis
12. Inverness Caledonian Thistle
13. Georgi Nemsadze
14. Barry Smith
15. Mark Fotheringham
16. Fabrizio Ravanelli
17. Airdrieonians, 3–2 after extra time
18. Aberdeen, 2–0
19. Livingston, in a 1–1 draw
20. Tam McManus

North of the Tay: Second Division 1

1. Theo Snelders
2. Twente Enschede
3. Lee Miller
4. Billy Dodds
5. Willie Miller
6. Duncan Shearer
7. Hans Gillhaus
8. Russell Anderson
9. The Dons
10. Stewart Milne
11. Ebbe Skovdahl
12. Steve Paterson
13. Willie Miller
14. Zander
15. Mark McGhee
16. Scott Leitch
17. Paul Bernard
18. 65
19. Young
20. Keith Wyness

North of the Tay: Second Division 2

1. 1983
2. Paul Hegarty
3. Celtic
4. £500,000
5. Craig Brewster
6. Rangers
7. St Mirren
8. Tannadice Park
9. Tannadice Street
10. Ivan Golac
11. He assaulted BBC reporter John Barnes
12. David Narey with 872 appearances
13. Falkirk
14. Gordon Chisholm
15. Kjell Olofsson
16. Trinidad and Tobago
17. Ralph Milne
18. Eddie Thompson
19. Peter Houston
20. 5th

North of the Tay: Second Division 3

1. Bob Shankly
2. Bobby Cox
3. 'The Dark Blues'
4. Argentinian
5. Georgian
6. Zurab Khizanishvili
7. Jocky Scott
8. *Hammy and the Hamsters*
9. Jesus Loves You
10. Julian Speroni
11. Jim Duffy
12. Glenn Larsen and John Sutton
13. Kevin McDonald
14. Ian Gilzean
15. Colin Cameron
16. Partick Thistle
17. Bobby Cox and Bob Shankly
18. Temuri Ketsbaia
19. Brent Sancho
20. Calum Melville

Other Scottish Clubs (Including Lower Division): Premier Division 1

1. Archie Gemmill
2. Brechin City's Glebe Park
3. Ian St John
4. It is named after the local farmer, Bruce McDiarmid, who donated the land on which the stadium stands
5. 1967
6. Cathkin Park
7. Andy Ritchie
8. Allan McGraw
9. Rangers
10. They lost 5–0
11. Kilmarnock
12. Chris Templeman
13. Motherwell, 2–0
14. Derek Townsley
15. Neale Cooper
16. John 'Sailor' Hunter
17. George Stevenson
18. Frank Beattie
19. Marcio Maximo
20. 4 months

Other Scottish Clubs (Including Lower Division): Premier Division 2

1. Sergei Baltacha
2. Hibs
3. Eddie Annand, from the penalty spot in extra time
4. Gordon Dalziel
5. Dumbarton
6. St Mirren
7. Dennis Wyness
8. Syd Puddefoot, from West Ham
9. Owen, Joe and Tommy Coyle
10. Murdo MacLeod
11. 2002
12. Steven Milne
13. Black and gold
14. 7
15. Nairn County
16. 'The Can Cans'
17. Wick Academy
18. Fosters
19. Halbeath Road
20. Elgin City

Other Scottish Clubs (Including Lower Division): Premier Division 3

1. Richie Hart
2. Raith Rovers
3. John Martin
4. Clachnacuddin
5. Motherwell
6. 4
7. Mixu Paatalainen
8. Alan Rough
9. 1971
10. Celtic, 4–1
11. Jimmy Bone
12. Gretna
13. Claude Anelka
14. The Ochils
15. Muirton Park
16. Paul Lambert
17. Harri Kampman
18. Finnish
19. Istvan Kozma
20. The £540,000 to Bordeaux remains the club's record fee

Scottish Clubs (Including Lower Division): First Division 1

1. Celtic
2. Stephen Kenny
3. Derry City
4. 2nd
5. Alex McLeish
6. Queen of the South, from the New Testament, Luke 11.31 'The queen of the south shall rise up at the judgement with the men of this generation, and condemn them'
7. Hibs
8. Adrian Sprott
9. John Lambie
10. The Ancell Babes
11. Liverpool
12. Willie McLean (1974–77) and Tommy McLean (1984–94)
13. The origins of the club are linked with the development of the steel industry in the area and many of the original shareholders worked for local steel companies
14. Willie Waddell
15. 8
16. Alex Ferguson
17. Ian Ferguson
18. Steven Naismith
19. Douglas Rae
20. Joe Miller

Scottish Clubs (Including Lower Division): First Division 2

1. Boghead Park
2. The Strathclyde Homes Stadium
3. Kevin Kyle
4. Kilmarnock
5. Alex Totten
6. True. He once played against Falkirk in a fundraiser in season 1955–56
7. Eddie May
8. Inverness Caledonian and Inverness Thistle
9. Palmerston Park
10. 'The Bully Wee'
11. Shawfield
12. Kirkcaldy
13. 36–0
14. Kilmarnock and Ayr United
15. Brooks Mileson
16. Queens Park
17. Hampden Park
18. Burnley
19. Jim Leishman
20. James McCarthy

Junior Football: Premier Division

1. Ardeer Thistle, Armadale Thistle, Bathgate Thistle, Burghead Thistle, Dalkeith Thistle, Dalry Thistle, East Kilbride Thistle, Kirriemuir Thistle, Largs Thistle, Larkhall Thistle, Lugar Boswell Thistle, North Forres Thistle, Scone Thistle, Hill of Beath Hawthorn, Oakley United, Thornton Hibs, Bonnyrigg Rose, Linlithgow Rose, Montrose Roselea, Crossgates Primrose, Dundee Violet, Dundonald Bluebell
2. Shawfield Juniors, Baillieston Juniors, Bridgeton Waverley and Dennistoun Waverley
3. Helenslea Park, Springfield Park and Kelvinvale Park
4. Camelon would be taking on Newtongrange Star at Glenrothes' home ground
5. 10
6. Tommy Gemmell – Coltness
   Bobby Murdoch – Cambuslang Rangers (loaned out)
   Billy McNeill – Blantyre Vics
   John Clark – Larkhall Thistle
   Jimmy Johnstone – Blantyre Celtic
   Willie Wallace – Kilsyth Rangers
   Stevie Chalmers – Kirkintilloch Rob Roy and Ashfield
   Bertie Auld – Maryhill Harp
   Bobby Lennox – Ardeer Recs
   John Fallon – Fauldhouse United
7. Hill of Beath, Hawthorn and Armadale Thistle respectively
8. Emirates airline
9. Shettleston
10. Auchinleck Talbot
11. 8
12. Bo'ness United's Newtown Park has a stated capacity of 7500
13. The club is named after a house in Burnside where the founder members met to hold the first club meeting.
14. Auchinleck Talbot, 3 wins (1986–88)
15. Cambuslang Rangers, 11 final appearances
16. As recognition of their feat in becoming the first Junior club to win 100 trophies
17. Pollok
18. Sunnybank (1954) and Banks O'Dee (1955)
19. Billy Young, George Gemmell, Sam McCulloch, Ross Findlay and Kenny Patterson
20. Yoker Athletic

Junior Football: First Division 1

1. 1977
2. Kilbirnie Ladeside and Kirkintilloch Rob Roy
3. 1886
4. True, he played 2 seasons for Bonnyrigg Rose
5. Newtongrange Star
6. 78,000. The official attendance was 77,650
7. Blantyre Vics
8. Newslandsfield Park
9. 3
10. Blue and white
11. Carmuirs Park
12. Frank McAvennie
13. 'Lade' is a Scots word for a burn or a small watercourse
14. Tommy Walker
15. Neil Watt
16. Dave Baikie
17. Tayport
18. True. They knocked them out in the first round in 1897
19. James Grady
20. Lord Talbot de Malahide, who gave them their ground

Junior Football: First Division 2

1. Spain Park, Aberdeen
2. Rugby Park
3. Cumnock, 2–1
4. Paul McGrillen
5. It was stolen and later found buried in a bing
6. Campbell Money
7. Panmure
8. Glenafton Athletic
9. Archie Gemmill
10. Hannah Park
11. Whitburn
12. 2007
13. Pollok, Girvan, Culter and Linlithgow Rose
14. Linlithgow Rose
15. Queen of the South
16. 4–0
17. Benburb
18. Lanark United
19. Jock Finlayson of Hill of Beath
20. Portsmouth, hence the reason why the silverware was initially known as the Pompey Cup

Scottish Rugby: Premier Division 1

1. All 3 were Scottish: Alex Frew, the South Africa captain, was a doctor from Kilmarnock who had emigrated to Transvaal; the Lions captain, Mark Morrison, was a Scot; and the referee was Bill Donaldson, who won 6 caps for Scotland in the 1890s
2. William and Robert Burrell
3. Jim Calder
4. 5
5. Iain Paxton
6. They were relegated to the Second Division for the first time in their history
7. Jim Telfer
8. Sandy Carmichael
9. Glenalmond College
10. Ian McLauchlan
11. 1873
12. Edinburgh University, Glasgow University, St Andrews University, Glasgow Academicals, the Royal High School, West of Scotland, and the Merchistonians
13. David Bedell-Sivright
14. 1875
15. Ian McGeechan
16. Football. He played for numerous Scottish clubs and also represented Scotland
17. 20–20
18. 8
19. Scotland, England, France, Australia
20. Ian Smith

Scottish Rugby: Premier Division 2

1. 104,000
2. Andy Nicol and Gavin Hastings
3. England. Scotland won 21–16
4. Japan
5. The game finished 0–0
6. Eddie O'Sullivan
7. Chris Paterson, with 6 penalties
8. 'Teapot'
9. He was a blacksmith
10. Hawick
11. 10
12. 7
13. Shane Williams
14. Mike Blair
15. 1974 and 77
16. Bill MacLagan (1891), Mark Morrison (1903), David Bedell-Sivright (1904), David MacMyn (1927), Arthur Smith (1962), Mike Campbell-Lamerton (1966), Finlay Calder (1989), Gavin Hastings (1993)
17. Andy Reed
18. Roger Uttley
19. The SRU refused to allow any Scottish players to travel after a row over expenses with New Zealand dating back to 1905
20. Ian Smith and Tony Stanger

Scottish Rugby: Premier Division 3

1. The 20–3 first Test defeat by New Zealand
2. Roy Kinnear
3. Archie
4. Cambridge
5. Adam 'Ned' Haig
6. 1883
7. Alexander and Francis Crombie
8. 1871
9. Raeburn Place, home of Edinburgh Accies
10. Angus Buchanan
11. Scotland with a goal and a try to a solitary England try
12. 20
13. Jim Renwick
14. Bill McLaren, shortly after the legendary commentator died in 2010
15. Colin Deans
16. Wilson Shaw
17. Arthur Smith
18. Australia
19. Poynder Park
20. 1994

Scottish Rugby: Premier Division 4

1. Argentinian
2. Bristol
3. Stadio Flaminio, Rome
4. 2001–02
5. Glasgow, losing 35–13
6. 2003–04. Edinburgh – 3rd bottom, Glasgow – 2nd bottom, Borders – bottom
7. 2004–05
8. Thom Evans with 9
9. Edinburgh, second to Munster in 2008–9
10. Dan Parks with 197 points
11. Dan Parks with 159 points
12. Chris Paterson with 159 points
13. 2003–04
14. Dan Parks with 1027 points. (Second is Felipe Contepomi with 877 points, as of March 2010)
15. 640 (as of March 2010)
16. 2006–07
17. Simon Webster with 28 for Edinburgh, 5th overall behind Tommy Bowe with 35
18. Alistair Kellock with 112: Edinburgh 57, Glasgow 55 (as of March 2010)
19. Leinster, Munster, Ulster, Connaught, Ospreys, Dragons, Blues and Scarlets
20. Tim Visser.

Scottish Rugby: First Division 1

1. John Leslie
2. 9 seconds
3. Scotland, 33–20
4. 52
5. False. Hampden has hosted three rugby internationals, in 1896, 1906 and 2004
6. Jim Telfer
7. Craig Chalmers
8. Wales
9. Rob Wainright
10. Gregor Townsend
11. 61
12. 6 ft 2 in
13. 20
14. 18
15. It was the most number of points scored by any debutant in Scotland's history
16. Craig Chalmers
17. Gavin Hastings
18. Jeremy Guscott
19. Rob Andrew
20. Merchiston Castle

Scottish Rugby: First Division 2

1. G P S MacPherson
2. Herbert Waddell
3. At the recently opened Murrayfield
4. South Africa
5. 28
6. Finlay Calder
7. Western Samoa, 28–6
8. Rob Andrew
9. Jim Calder
10. Grant Fox
11. John Jeffrey
12. True. He went to school in Portobello, Edinburgh
13. Selkirk
14. Alan Tait
15. Through his grandmother who was born in the Channel Islands, meaning he could choose whichever home nation he wished
16. 3
17. He wanted all of Scotland's top players to be playing their rugby in Scotland
18. Alan Lawson
19. 26 years
20. 'Del Boy'

Scottish Rugby: First Division 3

1. The Toonie Flip
2. 82
3. Jim Craig, the defender who won the European Cup with Celtic in 1967
4. 1982, when they defeated them 12–7 in Brisbane
5. They picked up the wooden spoon
6. Ian McGeechan and Jim Telfer
7. Alan Bulloch
8. Sandy Carmichael
9. 1993
10. France
11. 1999
12. Gavin Hastings
13. True. He scored 2 tries for the Lions, in the 2nd and 3rd Tests in South Africa in 1974
14. London Scottish
15. Dan Parks
16. Australia
17. His maternal grandmother comes from Ayrshire
18. Drink driving. He was subsequently banned from driving for 18 months
19. 16–12 to Italy
20. Mirco Bergamasco

Scottish Rugby: First Division 4

1. Melrose
2. Lewis Calder
3. Netherdale
4. He was headmaster at Hawick High
5. Iain Milne
6. Mathieu Bastareaud
7. Marcus di Rollo
8. Canada
9. Hefin
10. The Welshman now plays for Scotland's Sevens team and is therefore ineligible for the country of his birth
11. Ian McLauchlan
12. 'Mossy'
13. Heriot's
14. Edinburgh Accies
15. Raeburn Place
16. Mike Blair and Alistair Kellock
17. The Five Nations and the Home Championship
18. 1999 and Scotland
19. 1939
20. 1920 and 1924

Scottish Rugby: Second Division 1

1. Andy Robinson
2. English
3. Ireland
4. Dan Parks
5. Johnnie Beattie
6. Bill McLaren
7. Thom Evans
8. 13–7
9. Tony Stanger
10. David Sole
11. Will Carling
12. Ian McGeechan
13. Matt Williams
14. Australian
15. Phil
16. 1984
17. France, 21–12
18. Peter Dods
19. Gala
20. Frank Hadden

Scottish Rugby: Second Division 2

1. Chris Paterson
2. Johnnie Beattie. His father John won 25 caps playing for Scotland as No.8
3. Euan Murray
4. Calder
5. Jim Calder
6. Stand-off
7. Melrose
8. Kenny Logan
9. Gabby Logan (nee Yorath), the TV presenter
10. 'The Great White Shark' or 'JJ'
11. He was a farmer
12. New Zealand
13. 2
14. Edinburgh and Glasgow Warriors
15. Head coach of Edinburgh
16. Firhill
17. Sean Lineen
18. John and Martin Leslie
19. New Zealand
20. 4th

Scottish Rugby: Second Division 3

1. Gordon McKie
2. 1925
3. The Calcutta Cup
4. Simon Taylor
5. Andy Nicol
6. Gavin Hastings
7. 'Flower of Scotland'
8. Japan
9. Jonah Lomu
10. New Zealand, 30–3
11. True. He won 7 caps on the wing as an Edinburgh University student
12. Gavin Hastings
13. Andy Irvine. His total of 209 points took him past All Black Don Clarke's tally of 207
14. Milne
15. Peter Dods
16. 25–25
17. 'Broon frae Troon'
18. The All Blacks, 48–30
19. South Africa
20. Southwell

Scottish Rugby: Second Division 4

1. George
2. Heriot's FP
3. 'Rud'
4. Princess Anne
5. Sir David Murray
6. Thom Evans
7. Newcastle
8. London Scottish
9. White
10. Australia
11. Melrose
12. True
13. Ulster
14. Jonny Wilkinson
15. The thistle
16. Chris Cusiter
17. Lamont
18. Border Reivers
19. The Greenyards
20. Australia

Scottish Golf: Premier Division 1

1. George Duncan 1931
   Eric Brown 1969 and 1971
   Bernard Gallacher 1991, 1993 and 1995
   Sam Torrance 2002
   Colin Montgomerie 2010
2. Played 4, won 4
3. Played 4, lost 4
4. It was the first-ever tie. It finished 16–16
5. 8
6. Royal Burgess 1735
   Honourable Company of Edinburgh Golfers 1744
   Royal and Ancient St Andrews 1754
7. Carnoustie, 7421 yards in 2007
8. 7: Carnoustie, St Andrews, Turnberry, Royal Troon, Prestwick, Muirfield and Musselburgh
9. St Andrews (28) and Prestwick (24)
10. Carnoustie (7) and Turnberry (3)
11. St Andrews, 1955 and 1958
12. Carnoustie 1975, Turnberry 1977, Muirfield 1980, Troon 1982
13. Jack Newton
14. Prestwick
15. 1860
16. Willie Park snr. of Musselburgh
17. Old Tom Morris, of Prestwick
18. 12
19. James Anderson (1877–89)
    Young Tom Morris (1868–70)
    Peter Thomson (1954–56)
20. Willie Anderson

Scottish Golf: Premier Division 2

1. 3
2. Tom Morris jnr.
3. 4: 1868, 69, 70 and 72 (it was not competed for in 1871)
4. 1873
5. Tom Kidd
6. 6
7. Sam Snead at St Andrews
8. 'Slammin' Sam'
9. Carnoustie
10. Eric Brown
11. Muirfield
12. 3: in 1959, 68 and 74
13. Kel Nagle
14. Troon
15. Tony Lema
16. All 3: 1966 at Muirfield and 1970 and 78 at St Andrews
17. Tom Weiskopf
18. Nick Price
19. Tom Watson
20. True

Other Sports

9. Who is this young Scots golfer?

Answers on page 240

10. Who is this Scots motor-racing driver?

Answers on page 240

Other Sports

11. How many gold medals did Scots cyclist Chris Hoy win at the Beijing Olympics?

Answers on page 240

12. Name these 4 Scottish snooker players.

Answers on page 240

Other Sports

13. Who is this Scottish curler?

Answers on page 240

14.   In which event did Scot Shirley Robertson win 2 Olympics gold medals?

Answers on page 240

15. Who is this Scottish former ice-hockey star?

Answers on page 240

16. Who is this Scottish former long-distance world champion?

Answers on page 240

Scottish Golf: Premier Division 3

1. False
2. Tommy Armour
3. Royal Troon
4. Mark Calcavecchia, Wayne Grady and Greg Norman
5. Mark Calcavecchia
6. Muirfield
7. A No.4 iron
8. 159
9. 1993, at Royal St George's
10. Royal Dornoch
11. Gene Sarazen
12. 14
13. 28
14. Bradley Dredge in the 2006 Dunhill Links, and Mikko Ilonen in the 2009 Dunhill Links
15. 8
16. 19 under
17. Ernie Els and Thomas Bjorn
18. Colin Montgomerie, who finished on a 5-under-par total of 283
19. 81
20. 65

Scottish Golf: Premier Division 4

1. Ernie Els, Thomas Levet, Stuart Appleby and Steve Elkington
2. Lee Westwood
3. The Honda Classic
4. 10
5. Young Tom Morris
6. The Portuguese Open
7. 1999
8. Tom Kite
9. Ernie Els
10. Steve Elkington
11. 1894
12. Sandwich
13. Sandy Lyle
14. Tommy Nakajima
15. Muirfield
16. Jessie Valentine
17. Belle Robertson
18. Dean Robertson
19. Kiawah Island
20. USA

Scottish Golf: Premier Division 5

1. Jeff Sluman
2. 79
3. Gregory Havret (2007) and Thomas Levet (2004)
4. Johan Edfors
5. Tom Clark
6. 1996
7. Old Tom Morris, in 1867, aged 46
8. George Duncan
9. 150–1
10. At the Catalan Open
11. 21
12. 1985
13. Paul Lawrie
14. Brookline
15. Ross Bain
16. 1960
17. Doug McGuigan
18. Gary Orr
19. Caithness
20. 1.68-inch ball

Scottish Golf: First Division 1

1. Sandy Lyle
2. 1988
3. 3
4. 10 strokes
5. Jean van de Velde and Justin Leonard
6. Royal Troon
7. It is the shortest hole in Open Championship golf at 126 yards
8. 1984
9. St Andrews
10. 8
11. 7
12. Lee Westwood, in 2000
13. Daniel
14. Lee Trevino
15. 1985 at Royal St George's
16. 27
17. Payne Stewart
18. Turnberry
19. It was the first time the Open had been held at Turnberry
20. 1977

Scottish Golf: First Division 2

1. Greg Norman
2. 5
3. Walter Hagen
4. 5
5. Paul Azinger
6. Tom Weiskopf
7. Nick Faldo
8. Nick Price
9. Jesper Parnevik
10. John Daly and Costantino Rocca
11. John Daly
12. Justin Leonard
13. Colin Montgomerie
14. The Barry Burn
15. Carnoustie's 6th hole
16. Stuart Wilson
17. Ernie Els
18. Thomas Levet
19. 5
20. Jose Maria Olazabal

Scottish Golf: First Division 3

1. Eric Ramsay
2. Rory McIlroy
3. Doug Sanders
4. Colin Montgomerie
5. 1754
6. Sandy Lyle
7. 6 wins (and 2 halves)
8. 8
9. 6
10. Bernhard Langer
11. The Swilcan Burn
12. 1987
13. Scott Drummond
14. Marc Warren
15. 31
16. Ernie Els and Loren Roberts
17. Ernie Els
18. Geoff Ogilvy, of Australia
19. Winged Foot
20. The United States Golf Association

Scottish Golf: First Division 4

1. Sam Torrance
2. Ernie Els, in 2000 and 03
3. Graeme McDowell
4. False
5. Thomas Bjorn
6. His mother Elizabeth, who died of cancer in 1991
7. Mhairi McKay
8. Sam Torrance
9. Stephen Gallacher
10. 2001
11. Sandy Lyle
12. Aberdeen Asset Management
13. Adam Hunter
14. Alastair Forsyth
15. Martin Laird
16. Lloyd and Elliot Saltman
17. Zack Saltman
18. Carly Booth
19. 17
20. Andrew Oldcorn, aged 41

Scottish Golf: Second Division 1

1. The Claret Jug
2. The Road Hole
3. The Ailsa course at Turnberry
4. Colin Montgomerie
5. Lloyd Saltman
6. Colin Montgomerie
7. Bob Torrance
8. Padraig Harrington, who Torrance has helped to Major success
9. Royal Troon
10. Todd Hamilton
11. Asia
12. Ernie Els
13. Padraig Harrington
14. Sergio Garcia
15. Carnoustie
16. Peter Alliss
17. Royal Troon
18. St Andrews
19. False, he was born in England
20. Colin Montgomerie

Scottish Golf: Second Division 2	Scottish Cricket: Premier Division 1
1. Richie Ramsay	1. Peter Such
2. Monty	2. John Emburey
3. Loch Lomond	3. Mike Denness
4. Dormie	4. Essex and Kent
5. Martin Kaymer	5. In his capacity as an ICC match referee, he sanctioned 6 Indian players, including Sachin Tendulkar, on their tour of South Africa
6. True	
7. Matthew	
8. The Women's British Open	
9. Royal Lytham and St Annes	6. Aberdeenshire
10. Moodie	7. Alma Hunt
11. Turnberry	8. 1882
12. Tom Watson	9. Leslie M Balfour-Melville
13. Stewart Cink	10. Legendary wicketkeeper Rod Marsh
14. He missed the cut for only the second time in a Major since he turned professional in 1996	11. Hunter Cosh
	12. J M Barrie
	13. John Blair
15. St Andrews, Carnoustie and Kingsbarns	14. James Aitchison
16. False. He won it in 2005	15. Mannofield, Aberdeen, on 17 and 18 September 1948
17. Aberdeen	16. 123
18. A Ferrari	17. 1998
19. Loch Lomond	18. Pakistan
20. False	19. New Zealand and Kenya
	20. Craig Wright

Scottish Cricket: Premier Division 2

1. Archie Jackson, whose family emigrated to Sydney when he was young
2. George Goddard
3. Grange
4. Northamptonshire
5. Gordon Greenidge
6. Greenock
7. John Kerr
8. Murray McDermott, who came on for Hearts' Henry Smith in a UEFA Cup tie against St Patrick's of Dublin in September 1988
9. Penicuik
10. Ross County
11. 1909
12. They shared the trophy after bad weather meant they ran out of dates to play it
13. 5
14. Uddingston
15. Gordon Greenidge, Desmond Haynes and Malcolm Marshall
16. 1785
17. Shaw Park, Alloa
18. By English soldiers garrisoned in the country in the years following the Jacobite rising of 1745
19. Dougie Brown
20. The Namibian team

Scottish Cricket: First Division 1

1. Brian Hardie
2. 6
3. 5
4. Richard Blakey
5. Aberdeenshire
6. James Aitchison
7. He was a minister
8. Asim Butt
9. He tested positive for the drug ecstasy
10. Berwick
11. Hector Blackburn
12. Boroughmuir
13. James Brinkley
14. Corstorphine
15. Myreside
16. The Ship Inn (Elie) XI
17. Shaun Maloney
18. One, in England's first Test innings defeat in the 1999–2000 tour of South Africa
19. South Africa and New Zealand
20. Bottom, with zero points

Scottish Cricket: First Division 2

1. Freuchie
2. Rowledge, of Surrey
3. David Christie
4. There was a street – Christiegait – named after him in Freuchie
5. 1959, against Warwickshire
6. Galashiels
7. Grange
8. Lancashire
9. Ireland
10. Worcestershire
11. Irvin Iffla
12. Rossie Priory
13. Hamish McAlpine
14. Morrison Zuill
15. Ireland
16. 2004
17. Canada
18. Gavin Hamilton
19. John Blain
20. Ferguslie

Scottish Cricket: Second Division

1. The Saltires
2. Drumpellier
3. Rahul Dravid
4. 3
5. None
6. Titwood, in Pollokshields, Glasgow
7. Twice
8. Grange Loan, in Edinburgh
9. Gavin Hamilton
10. Roddy Smith
11. Douglas
12. Craig Wright
13. Greig Williamson
14. Australia, South Africa and the Netherlands
15. None
16. The West Indies
17. True
18. Kelso (records date back to 1820)
19. Edinburgh
20. Keith Oliver

Scottish Athletics: Premier Division 1

1. 28
2. 10.11 seconds
3. Triple jump
4. Henry
5. Bronze
6. Jackson Scholz
7. Peter Radford, who won bronze in Rome in 1960
8. Pietro Mennea, of Italy
9. Birmingham
10. Birchfield Harriers
11. Athens
12. Lachie Stewart (no relation)
13. He ran a new European, British and Scottish record time of 13 minutes 22.8 seconds
14. Ian McCafferty
15. Kip Keino
16. 5th
17. 6th
18. Don Quarrie
19. Gold
20. 2: in the 100 metres and 200 metres

Scottish Athletics: Premier Division 2

1. 25
2. 4th
3. Launceston Elliot won a weightlifting gold medal in 1896 in Athens
4. Olga Bondarenko, of Russia
5. 5th
6. 16th
7. Silver
8. Wyndham Halswelle
9. 400 metres
10. It was the one and only time an Olympic event had been decided by a walkover. Halswelle ran solo following a rerun of the race. Previously, the Scot had been blocked by John Carpenter on the finishing straight. The American was disqualified and the two other Americans – the only other competitors – boycotted the rerun two days later
11. Johnny McGough
12. Arthur Robertson
13. He was controversially disqualified in the semi-final for excessive physical contact
14. Last. He caught the foot of another competitor and was injured
15. The 4 x 400 metres relay
16. Toronto
17. Glasgow
18. David Sharpe
19. Split
20. Gemma Nicol

Scottish Athletics: Premier Division 3

1. David Jenkins, Allan Wells and Drew McMaster
2. Bronze, in the 100 metres, 200 metres and 4 x 100 metres relay
3. Lynsey Sharp
4. Hayley Haining
5. Menzies Campbell
6. He became a politician and later led the Liberal Democrat party
7. Graham Williamson
8. Tom Hanlon
9. Darren Ritchie in 2004
10. Shirley Webb
11. Battleaxe, the Gladiator
12. Allan Scott
13. Silver
14. His late brother, Ross, who died of an anaphylactic shock after a severe allergic reaction to a peanut in 1999
15. 29
16. 6th
17. James Campbell
18. 77 metres. He threw 76.71 metres
19. Jayne Nisbet
20. Stephanie Twell

Scottish Athletics: First Division 1

1. Lenin Stadium
2. Lane 8
3. 10.25 seconds
4. Silvio Leonard
5. Cuban
6. Harold Abrahams in Paris, 1924
7. Peter
8. Mary
9. 1975
10. Bronze
11. 7th
12. China
13. He became a missionary
14. Lachie Stewart
15. Rosemary Stirling
16. Rosemary Payne
17. They were opposed to apartheid in sport
18. Liz McColgan (nee Lynch)
19. Tokyo
20. University of Alabama

Scottish Athletics: First Division 2

1. Yvonne Murray
2. Bronze
3. Dougie Walker
4. 'The Bellshill Bullet'
5. Steve Cram
6. Sebastian Coe and Steve Cram
7. Stuttgart
8. Tommy Boyle
9. 4
10. Stephanie Cook
11. Ian McCafferty
12. Alistair McCorquodale
13. The High Jump
14. 400 metres Hurdles
15. The 4 x 400 metres Relay
16. Ian Mackie
17. Sinead Dudgeon
18. Allison Curbishley
19. Elliot Bunney
20. Melanie Neef. Her father was Gerry Neef

Scottish Athletics: Second Division

1. Edinburgh
2. *Chariots of Fire*
3. Rugby. He won 7 caps
4. 100 metres
5. The heats fell on a Sunday and Liddell refused to take part as he was a Christian and wanted to respect the Sabbath
6. 400 metres
7. Gold
8. It was a new Olympic record
9. Glasgow
10. Abuja in Nigeria
11. Dundee
12. Peter McColgan
13. Eilish McColgan
14. New York
15. He became a police officer
16. Lee McConnell
17. Andrew Lemoncello
18. Lee McConnell, in the individual 400 metres
19. Linsey Macdonald
20. Jimmy Bryce

Scottish Horseracing: Premier Division 1

1. George H Boyd
2. 2
3. 3
4. Captain Gerald Armstrong
5. 1979
6. Troy
7. Henbit
8. 54
9. Sandy Barclay
10. 2nd – Piggott beat him by a length and a half
11. 20
12. Carl Llewellyn
13. Run For Paddy
14. 1867
15. Couvrefeu II
16. Southern Hero
17. Rubstic
18. John Leadbetter, at Denholm in the Borders
19. Nigel Angus
20. The race was run at Ayr after the track at Doncaster was declared unfit

Scottish Horseracing: Premier Division 2

1. Sea Pigeon
2. Mark Johnston
3. Hamilton Park on 18 July 1947
4. Dizzy, trained by Peter Monteith and ridden by Tony Dobbin
5. Harry Hastings, ridden by Chris Grant
6. The winner was called Ayrshire
7. Love Divine
8. Celtic Giant (1999), Freetown (2002)
9. Ayr racecourse
10. April
11. Adrian Maguire
12. Belmont King
13. Paul Nicholls
14. 2
15. Captain Dibble (1992), Little Polveir (1987)
16. Iris de Balme
17. 5
18. 1972, 73, 78, 80 and 83
19. Sandy Struthers
20. Take Control

Scottish Horseracing: First Division 1

1. Harry Bell
2. Ken Oliver
3. Pappageno's Cottage (1963), The Spaniard (1970), Young Ash Leaf (1971), Fighting Fit (1979), Cockle Strand (1982)
4. Sanvina (1950)
5. 'The Benign Bishop'
6. Graham and Charlie Macmillan
7. 2
8. 1972
9. 1962
10. High Top
11. Lester Piggott
12. Bogside Racecourse
13. Hello Bud
14. Paddy Brennan
15. P J McDonald
16. Adrian Maguire
17. Queen's Taste
18. Little Polveir
19. Earth Summit
20. Cree Lodge

Scottish Horseracing: First Division 2

1. Willie Carson
2. Henry Cecil
3. It is the richest sprint handicap in Europe
4. Jenny Pitman, Willsford (1995) and Lavinia Taylor, Gingembre (2001)
5. Peter Niven (1002)
6. Big Timer
7. Linda Perratt
8. Mark Johnston
9. Mister Baileys
10. It was the fastest winning time, 1 minute 35.08 seconds
11. Richard Quinn
12. 1990
13. 1995
14. The British Horseracing Board switched the race from Ayr's traditional Glasgow Holiday Monday fixture to the following week
15. 3: 2003–05
16. *The Daily Record*
17. Sir Michael Stoute
18. Candleriggs
19. Ferguson's father worked to build a ship of the same name on the River Clyde
20. Broomielaw

Scottish Horseracing: Second Division

1. Stirling
2. Sandy Barclay
3. Pat Eddery
4. 1977
5. It was the Queen's Silver Jubilee
6. Joe Mercer
7. 5
8. Ayr, Hamilton Park, Kelso, Musselburgh and Perth
9. Coral
10. 27
11. Ayr racecourse
12. Red Rum
13. 1974
14. Len Lungo
15. 63
16. Six furlongs
17. Frankie Dettori
18. Rock of Gibraltar
19. Lomond
20. T Quinn

Scottish Boxing: Premier Division 1

1. Ruben Navarro and Ismael Laguna
2. 7
3. Guts Ishimatsu (he was originally called Ishimatsu Suzuki)
4. *The Joe Louis Story*
5. Sparta
6. *The Tartan Legend*
7. Johnny Hill
8. He beat the US fighter Newsboy Brown over 15 rounds in London on August 1928
9. Sammy Wilson
10. Jim Campbell
11. Jackie Jurich, the American fighter
12. He did not make the weight and was stripped of the title before the fight. He actually stopped the American in the 12th round
13. Jim Warnock
14. Aurel Toma
15. Peter Keenan
16. Jonathan Dele
17. He wanted to turn professional
18. 4
19. Dick McTaggart
20. In 1956 at the Melbourne Olympics

Scottish Boxing: Premier Division 2

1. He wanted to be a jockey when he was a child
2. Thomas McGowan
3. Joe Gans, after the great American lightweight boxer of the late 19th and early 20th century
4. Chartchai Chionoi
5. Joe Kelly
6. Eyup Khan of Turkey
7. Wayne McCullough
8. It broke the 61-year-old record for the quickest knockout. Harrison took less than a minute. The previous holder was Scot Jackie Paterson, who knocked out Peter Kane in 90 seconds in 1943
9. It was his record 6th world-title fight, one more than Jim Watt managed
10. Bobby Neill – who took Alan Minter and Lloyd Honeyghan to their titles
11. Featherweight
12. Super featherweight
13. Joan Guzmán pulled out of their fight and Arthur was awarded the title
14. Nicky Cooke of England was given the decision which was bitterly disputed by Arthur in the Manchester Arena. Arthur claimed that the 3 English judges had favoured the Englishman
15. They are the only two former world champions never to have won a world-title fight. Norton was awarded the world title when Leon Spinks refused to fight him. He then lost the title in his next fight. Arthur's fight with Nicky Cooke was his first defence
16. Chic Calderwood
17. Young Muttley
18. Tommy Milligan (1924), Johnny Brown (1925), Jake Kilrain (1936), Gary Jacobs (1993)
19. Gary McArthur
20. Barry Morrison

Scottish Boxing: First Division 1

1. Maurice Cullen
2. Miguel Valasquez
3. Ismael Laguna
4. Panamanian
5. Puerto Rico
6. He won on a points decision, 145–144
7. 61
8. 27
9. Antonio Puddu
10. Small Montana
11. Wembley
12. 33
13. Jackie Paterson
14. John 'Rinty' Monaghan
15. Peter Keenan
16. Alfredo Pitalua
17. Colombia
18. 30
19. Ibrox Stadium
20. Alexis Arguello, of Nicaragua

Scottish Boxing: First Division 2

1. Salvatore Fanni
2. Isdiro Perez, of Mexico
3. Clinton won on points
4. Tommy Gilmour
5. Julio Pablo Chacon
6. Argentina
7. Braehead Arena
8. Peter Harrison
9. Frank Maloney
10. 'The Real McCoy'
11. Frank Warren
12. WBU (World Boxing Union)
13. Lightweight
14. Ryan Barrett
15. Paul Weir
16. WBO Minimum Weight
17. John Simpson
18. Paul Truscott
19. Hampden Park
20. Lou Savarese

Scottish Boxing: Second Division

1. Edinburgh
2. Roberto Duran
3. In the 13th round Buchanan claimed Duran had knocked him down with a low blow
4. Jim Watt
5. Buchanan beat Watt on a points decision in Glasgow
6. The Gorbals
7. Jackie Brown
8. Manchester
9. 8
10. 1979
11. The Kelvin Hall, Glasgow
12. Walter McGowan
13. Croy
14. Billy Clinton
15. The 1984 Los Angeles Olympic Games
16. The Kelvin Hall, Glasgow
17. St Andrew's Sporting Club, Glasgow
18. Tommy Gilmour
19. Scott Harrison
20. Edinburgh

Scottish Snooker: Premier Division 1

1. Stephen Hendry, John Higgins and Graeme Dott
2. Hendry – 7 times (1990–96 and 1999)
   John Higgins – 3 times (1998, 2007 and 2009)
   Graeme Dott – once (2006)
3. Grand Prix
4. 1994–95
5. 5
6. False
7. Jimmy White
8. David Roe
9. Jamie Cope
10. 2004 World Championship and 2005 Malta Cup
11. China Open
12. British Open
13. Dennis Taylor
14. 4 (1987, 1990, 91 and 95)
15. True – O'Sullivan has made 3 while Hendry has only made 2 (as of March 2010)
16. Alan McManus
17. 9–8
18. None
19. Neil Robertson
20. Fergal O'Brien

Scottish Snooker: Premier Division 2

1. The China Open
2. The European Open
3. 10–1
4. 1998
5. His quarter-final triumph over Mark Selby at the 2009 World Championships in which he came from 12–11 down to win the last 2 frames
6. 4
7. Jamie Burnett
8. It was the first break of 148 ever recorded in competition. It occurred in the second round of qualifying for the UK Championship
9. When he was snookered after a foul, Burnett nominated brown as his extra red, sank the brown again as his colour, potted all the red with 12 blacks, then 2 pinks and 1 blue before clearing the colours
10. Depression
11. John Rea
12. Walter Donaldson, from Coatbridge
13. Fred Davis
14. 9
15. Ronnie O'Sullivan
16. Chris Small
17. Drew Henry
18. Euan Henderson
19. Billy Snaddon
20. Paul McPhillips

Scottish Snooker: First Division 1

1. He defeated Mark Selby 18–13
2. It was the latest-ever finish to a World Final (00.54 am)
3. Stephen Maguire
4. He played in goal in a friendly football match with his fellow players before his opening game in Shanghai and broke his wrist
5. Ronnie O'Sullivan
6. Dott led 5–0
7. 21
8. He was the youngest-ever champion at the Crucible
9. Ken Doherty
10. Peter Ebdon
11. 18–17
12. Trailing 4–1 in a best of 19 frames match, O'Sullivan missed an easy red and immediately shook Hendry's hand to concede the match
13. Terry Griffiths
14. Stephen Maguire, after getting knocked out in the last 8 of the World Championship
15. Ryan Day
16. It was the first time he had won a ranking tournament on Scottish soil
17. Peter Ebdon beat him 10–8
18. Mark Allen
19. Water dripped onto the table
20. Williams won but he lost to Stephen Hendry in the final

Scottish Snooker: First Division 2

1. Shaun Murphy
2. Jimmy White
3. He broke his left arm after slipping in the toilet
4. Alex 'Hurricane' Higgins. Hendry, unaffected, beat Higgins 9–4
5. Ronnie O'Sullivan
6. He lost the 2010 final to Neil Robertson
7. Martin O'Neill, who was then the successful manager of Celtic. Dott supports their rivals, Rangers
8. Ronnie O'Sullivan
9. 17–11
10. Chris Small
11. Marcus Campbell
12. Stephen Maguire and Jamie Burnett
13. Jim Donnelly
14. 3
15. John Higgins
16. Alan McManus
17. The Motherwell Civic Centre
18. Aberdeen Exhibition and Conference Centre
19. The Scottish Exhibition and Conference Centre
20. The Kelvin Hall International Sports Arena

Scottish Snooker: Second Division

1. 'Wizard of Wishaw'
2. Graeme Dott
3. Ken Doherty
4. 18–12
5. He became world No.1
6. Peter Ebdon
7. 18–14
8. Hearts
9. 1985
10. Jimmy White
11. BBC Scotland Sports Personality of the Year
12. 'Angles'
13. betfred.com
14. Embassy
15. Celtic
16. 1979
17. Stephen Hendry and John Higgins
18. 40
19. Alan McManus
20. 110sport

Scottish Motorsport: Premier Division 1

1. Juan Pablo Montoya
2. BBC Scotland Sports Personality of the Year
3. Allan McNish
4. 2 times: in 1998 and 2008
5. 1968
6. Germany. He was racing in a Formula Two race in Hockenheim
7. Wolfgang von Trips
8. Jackie Stewart
9. Dario Franchitti
10. 1994
11. Ayrton Senna, who had died in 1994 in a crash at the San Marino Grand Prix
12. The Portuguese Grand Prix
13. His light aircraft was heading for Nice with 5 passengers on board when it crashed, killing the pilot and co–pilot. Coulthard miraculously survived
14. Australia
15. The Monaco Grand Prix
16. 2000 and 2002
17. Twynholm
18. Red Bull
19. The Monaco Grand Prix, where he finished 3rd
20. He donned a red Superman cap

Scottish Motorsport: Premier Division 2

1. Felipe Massa
2. 13
3. 5
4. Alister
5. Once, in 1995
6. Roger Clark
7. 3 times
8. He was killed when the helicopter he was flying crashed
9. Jimmy Stewart
10. Shooting
11. Stewart Grand Prix
12. Johnny Herbert
13. Jaguar racing
14. Dumbarton
15. Suzie Stoddart
16. Bob McGregor
17. 100 mph. McGregor recorded a speed of 101.03 mph in 1957
18. 6
19. Hawick
20. 3

Scottish Motorsport: Premier Division 3

1. Germany
2. Steve Hislop
3. Carl Fogarty
4. 2
5. 1995 and 2002
6. Yes, in 1990
7. 2003
8. They both came from Hawick and have statues erected to them in the town
9. Johnny Dumfries
10. 1984
11. True: he was a late addition to the Lotus team, in 1986
12. The Le Mans 24-hour race
13. A Silk Cut-sponsored Jaguar
14. Edinburgh businessman and racing driver David Murray, and mechanic Wilkie Wilkinson
15. The Le Mans 24 Hours
16. Ron Flockhart and Ninian Sanderson
17. Jaguar D-Type
18. The team's 2 cars finished 1st and 2nd, a feat rarely achieved by a private team
19. Hugh McCaig
20. Jimmy and Jackie Stewart

Scottish Motorsport: Premier Division 4

1. The Jack Young Memorial trophy
2. Jack Young
3. Peter Carr
4. Preston
5. 2200 points
6. 2003 and 2008
7. Ryan Fisher, Andrew Tully, Kevin Wolbert, Jozsef Tabaka, Kalle Katajisto, Max Dilger, William Lawson, Derek Sneddon, Aaron Summers and team captain Mathew Wethers.
8. Bernie Persson with a 9.31 average
9. 1928
10. Glasgow Tigers
11. 1987 and Workington
12. Ashfield
13. Travis McGowan, James Grieves, Josh Gradczonek, Robert Ksiezek, Lee Dicken, Jamie Courtney, Mitchell Davey
14. 1993 and 94
15. 2005 and 2006
16. Coatbridge
17. Ken le Breton (real name Francis) who died tragically in 1951 riding in Australia
18. Linlithgow
19. The Lions
20. St Mirren Stadium in Love St

Scottish Motorsport: First Division 1

1. Bathgate
2. The Indycar Series Driver Championship
3. Andretti Green Racing
4. The Indycar 500
5. Jim Clark
6. Ashley Judd
7. Marino
8. Celtic
9. Queen of the South
10. Jim Clark
11. 2 times: 1963 and 65
12. 3 times: 1969, 71 and 73
13. McLaren
14. Mika Hakkinen
15. He lives in Monaco
16. False: he won it in 2000
17. Michael Schumacher
18. Bulimia
19. Knockhill
20. Louise Aitken Walker

Scottish Motorsport: First Division 2

1. Innes Ireland
2. Niall Mackenzie
3. He is the only rider to have won 3 successive British Superbike titles
4. In 1980 he won the Sidecar World Championship
5. Benga Johansson
6. 4
7. 1982
8. Finland at the Imatra track
9. Armadale, since 1997
10. Matthew Wethers
11. 4: 2006, 07, 08 and 09
12. The Eagles
13. True, the Fife Lions. On their first meeting in 1965 they defeated the Colonial Tigers 44–33
14. The Australian Grand Prix
15. The Mercedes-powered Force India team
16. Dario Franchitti
17. The European F3 Championship
18. Sebastian Vettel
19. Lewis Hamilton
20. Bathgate in West Lothian

Scottish Swimming: Premier Division

1. A swimming cap
2. Wilkie came in 3rd to pick up a bronze medal
3. Andrew
4. She was selected for the British team at the 1988 Olympics in Seoul
5. 15
6. Gary Van Der Meulen
7. 7th
8. Bronze
9. Sue Rolph
10. Bobby McGregor
11. Dan Schollander
12. Elenor Gordon
13. Jack Wardrop
14. Catherine Brown (nee Gibson)
15. Lewis Smith
16. Caitlin McClatchey
17. David Carry
18. David Carry, Euan Dale, Robbie Renwick, Andy Hunter
19. Euan Dale
20. Ian Black

Scottish Swimming: First Division

1. Sri Lanka
2. The University of Miami in the United States
3. Silver
4. 2: one in the 200 metres Breaststroke and another in the 200 metres Individual Medley
5. John Hencken, of the USA
6. Dave Haller
7. Peter Heatly
8. Elenor Gordon
9. Kirsty Balfour
10. Another silver
11. Leisel Jones, of Australia
12. Alan McClatchey
13. Bronze, in the 4 x 200 metres Freestyle relay
14. He won 2 golds and a silver
15. Gregor Tait
16. Ian Black
17. 17
18. Graeme Smith
19. She was given an MBE
20. Gregor Tait

Scottish Swimming: Second Division

1. The 1976 Montreal Olympics
2. It was a world record
3. Silver
4. Ian Edmond
5. Alison Sheppard
6. The Milngavie and Bearsden club
7. The University of Stirling
8. England
9. Her parents, John and Louise, swam for Scotland in the 1970 and 1974 Olympics respectively
10. Miley
11. Her father, Patrick Miley
12. Jack McConnell
13. Tollcross
14. 12
15. 6
16. 2
17. The 200 metres and 400 metres Freestyle
18. David Wilkie in 1974
19. The 50 metres Freestyle
20. Doug Frost

Winter Sports: Premier Division

1. He was crowned World Junior Champion
2. 4
3. 3
4. Lockerbie
5. He is a dairy farmer
6. 2 times
7. Ben Kilner
8. 18th
9. Elise Christie
10. Gold
11. Nicola Minichiello
12. Pole Vault
13. No, she and Nicola Minichiello crashed out in their 3rd run
14. Finlay Mickel
15. 31
16. Andrew Noble
17. The Bonspiel
18. 3
19. Loch Leven (1) and the Lake of Menteith (2)
20. 7 ins

Winter Sports: First Division

1. Rhona Martin
2. The Stone of Destiny
3. Switzerland
4. Jackie Lockhart
5. Germany
6. Eve Muirhead
7. 19
8. Lesley McKenna
9. 30th
10. Alain Baxter
11. Bronze
12. He failed a drugs test
13. 'The Highlander'
14. Noel Baxter
15. Andrew Musgrave
16. Andrew Young
17. Huntly
18. All of them
19. David Murdoch, Ewan MacDonald, Peter Smith, Graeme Connal and Euan Byers
20. The Royal Caledonian Curling Club

Scottish Cycling: Premier Division 1

1. 4th
2. He was crowned King of the Mountains
3. Billy Bilsland
4. 2nd
5. *The Flying Scotsman*
6. 1993 and 94
7. Chris Boardman
8. 2: 1993 and 95
9. A washing machine
10. 'Old Faithful'
11. Swimmer Henry Taylor in 1908
12. Individual Sprint, Team Sprint and Keirin
13. 1 km Time Trial
14. *E.T. the Extra Terrestrial*
15. BMX racing
16. Team Sprint
17. Bran Flakes
18. BBC Sports Personality of the Year
19. Lewis Hamilton and Rebecca Adlington
20. Chris Hoy, Craig MacLean and Ross Edgar

Scottish Cycling: Premier Division 2

1. Mark Beaumont
2. 194 days (and 17 hours)
3. 81
4. The Prologue
5. The blood-booster EPO
6. He was World Time-Trial Champion
7. Malta
8. Fort William
9. Ruaridh Cunningham
10. 4X
11. Gavin Kennedy
12. James McCallum
13. He is an auxiliary nurse
14. Evan Oliphant
15. Ross Creber
16. Endure Racing
17. Mountain biking
18. They were named Britain's Toughest Family
19. Kate Cullen
20. She was the first Scotswoman to win a medal in a Commonwealth cycling event

Scottish Darts: Premier Division

1. Jocky Wilson
2. 1982 and 89
3. 4
4. The Jocky Wilson Cup in which Scotland's best players will play England's best
5. Eric Bristow 'the Crafty Cockney'
6. Les Wallace
7. He was the first left-hander to win the title and it was the 2nd time in 4 years that 2 unseeded players had contested the final
8. Marshall James of Wales 6–3
9. 'McDanger'. He also came out for his matches dressed in a kilt
10. 'Bravedart'
11. Robert Thornton
12. The Proclaimers – 'I'm Gonna Be (500 miles)'
13. Gary Anderson
14. The Welsh Players Championship in Newport
15. The British Matchplay. He also won the Golden Darts Championship that year.
16. Ross 'The Boss' Montgomery
17. John 'Hendo' Henderson
18. Chris Louden
19. Robert Taylor
20. Mike Veitch

Scottish Bowling: Premier Division 1

1. Queens Park
2. Alex Marshall
3. 5
4. 1999, 2003, 04, 07 and 08
5. None
6. 2: 1992 – Marshall and Corsie
   2000 – Marshall and Sneddon
7. 3: 1996 – Adrain, Wood and Logan
   2004 – Peacock, Wood and McIntyre
   2008 – Peacock, Wood and Hogg
8. George Adrain replaced Jim Candelet who was taken ill after two matches
9. Darren Burnett, in 2006
10. 1994, Richard Corsie
11. 3: 1989, 91 and 93
12. He is an entrepreneur in the leisure industry
13. John Watson
14. 1988 and 1997
15. 1966 in Kingston, Jamaica
16. Alex Marshall and Paul Foster
17. Joyce Lindores and Kay Moran
18. Alex Marshall and George Sneddon
19. Willie Wood
20. Alister Reid, Seafield

Scottish Bowling: Premier Division 2

1. Glenmavis
2. Paul Foster
3. Alex Marshall (4), Darren Burnett (11), David Gourley (13) and Stewart Anderson (18)
4. Alex Marshall
5. Darren Burnett
6. 1st – David Gourley
   2nd – Alex Marshall
   3rd – Paul Foster
7. Bob Sutherland.
8. 1998 and 2001
9. Yes, in 1996
10. First – David Gourley and second – Alex Marshall
11. 19
12. Bronze
13. Tony Allcock
14. Surprisingly, he never won it
15. 7
16. 14
17. 1966
18. He was involved in a dispute with the Scottish Bowls Association, who deemed him a professional
19. He claimed the greens were not up to scratch
20. 2004, at Ayr's Northfield complex

Trivia: Premier Division

1. Matt Busby: 24.75 years. Ferguson had been manager for 23.75 years
2. Tommy Docherty: December 1972 – June 1977
3. Bill Shankly – 15 years
   Kenny Dalglish – 6 years
   Graeme Souness – 3 years
4. George Graham, Bruce Rioch and Stewart Houston
5. Gordon Strachan
6. The East of Scotland League
7. Gretna 2008
8. Jocky Scott, by Dundee
9. Helmut Haller
10. Celtic, East Stirlingshire, Dundee United, East Fife and Kilmarnock
11. Hearts' Jimmy Murray against Yugoslavia in 1958
12. 7
13. Billy McNeill, Liam Brady, Lou Macari, Tommy Burns, Wim Jansen, Gordon Strachan and Tony Mowbray
14. Kilmarnock, Dundee United, Motherwell and Third Lanark
15. Scotsman: Alan McInally – Celtic, Aston Villa and Bayern Munich
    Welshman: Mark Hughes – Man United, Barcelona and Bayern Munich
    Irishmen: Roy Keane – Man United, Celtic and Nottingham Forest and Tony Cascarino – Celtic, Aston Villa and Marseille
16. Brian O'Neil (Wolfsburg), Scott Booth (Borussia Dortmund) and Garry O'Connor (Lokomotiv Moscow)
17. Evander Sno, Javier Sanchez Broto, Juninho, Tony Cascarino, Paolo di Canio, Frank Munro, Koki Mizuno and Landry N'Guemo
18. Cowdenbeath
19. Partick Thistle
20. Ian McCall

Trivia: First Division

1. Kenny Dalglish
2. Gretna F C
3. Peter Philips, son of Princess Anne and Mark Philips
4. Steve Clarke
5. Liz McColgan, having won the 10,000 metres at the Tokyo World Championships
6. David Weir
7. 39 years (and 329 days)
8. Jock 'Tiger' Shaw's record
9. 13
10. Swedish First Division side Helsingborg
11. Landskrona
12. 1975–76
13. 6
14. Peter MacDonald
15. Russell Anderson
16. John Barnes.
   Celtic under Barnes: played 29, won 19, drawn 2, lost 8. Win percentage – 66%
   Celtic under Mowbray: played 45, won 23, drawn 9, lost 13. Win percentage – 51%
17. *Pointless*, by Jeff Connor
18. *Hunting Grounds: a Scottish Football Safari*, by Gary Sutherland
19. Pie and Bovril
   www.pieandbovril.com
20. Gavin Strachan

Trivia: Second Division

1. Ian St John
2. Ferranti Thistle
3. Meadowbank Thistle
4. St Johnstone
5. Peter Nicol
6. Lorraine Kelly
7. Mark McGhee
8. Andy and Jamie Murray
9. Davis Love III
10. Willie Carson
11. Jim O'Brien
12. A shopping centre
13. Scott Arfield
14. Dean Windass
15. Andrew Oldcorn
16. 13
17. Csaba Laszlo
18. Maurice Ross
19. DaMarcus Beasley
20. Dumbarton, Stirling Albion, Gretna, Queen's Park, East Fife and Cowdenbeath

Scottish Tennis: First Division

1. Sanchez-Casal Academy
2. 2004
3. Sergiy Stakhovsky
4. Liezel Huber, of the USA
5. Thomas Johansson
6. Cramp
7. George Bastl and Radek Stepanek
8. David Nalbandian
9. 6 ft 3 in
10. Jamie Baker
11. She represented the USSR in both the Heptathlon and Pentathlon at the Olympic Games
12. He was a professional footballer
13. Third round, where she lost to Elena Likhovtseva
14. Kirsten Klipkens
15. Eric Butorac and Jamie Murray
16. 64
17. Graham Dyce
18. Leon Smith
19. Pato Alvarez
20. Fernando Gonzalez

Miscellaneous Sports: Premier Division 1

1. Dr John Cattanach
2. Shooting
3. Water Polo
4. 2
5. George Kerr
6. William Kinnear
7. Weightlifting
8. Graeme Randall
9. Gold
10. Silver
11. 3
12. Winifred Mason Wooldridge (nee Shaw)
13. Joyce Williams
14. 1893
15. 12
16. Scottish Hydro
17. The Dell
18. Red and blue hoops
19. Fort William
20. Gary Innes

Miscellaneous Sports: Premier Division 2

1. Their achievement of winning 20 successive league titles makes them the most successful team in the history of world sport
2. Derek Cameron
3. Kingussie, Newtonmore, Kyles and Fort William
4. 28
5. Steve Borthwick
6. Edinburgh Capitals and the Braehead Clan
7. Kyle Horne and Ben O'Connor
8. Mark Garside
9. Cody Rudkowsky
10. Owen Fussey
11. Doug Christiansen
12. 2007
13. Dundee Stars, Edinburgh Capitals, Fife Flyers, Paisley Pirates and Solway Sharks
14. Billingham Bombers and the Blackburn Hawks
15. Fife Flyers
16. All teams play each other twice but Edinburgh only play each team once for double points
17. He became the first British-born player to be drafted by an NHL team, the Edmonton Oilers
18. Murrayfield Racers
19. 1000
20. Manchester Phoenix

Miscellaneous Sports: Premier Division 3

1. Alistair McGregor
2. Vishal Marwaha
3. Fergus Dunn, forward
4. Emma Rochlin
5. Linda Clement
6. Kenny Bain
7. Australia, England, New Zealand, Canada
8. 4th
9. Graham
10. Chay Blyth
11. 92
12. He became the first person to sail westwards around the world against the prevailing winds and currents
13. Shirley Robertson
14. Sarah Ayton and Sarah Webb
15. They won gold in the Europe Class
16. Gold
17. The Yngling class
18. The Mexico Olympics in 1968
19. 3: gold in 1968, another gold in Munich in 1972 and a silver in Montreal in 1976
20. Bronze

Miscellaneous Sports: First Division 1

1. Sarah Clark
2. David Somerville
3. Boher Ash
4. The 1920s (it won it in 1928)
5. Shirley McIntosh
6. 4
7. Susan Jackson
8. Who became the first Scottish woman to win 2 Commonwealth Games Shooting golds in 2006?
9. Sheena Sharp
10. 52
11. Ian Marsden
12. Rita
13. Robert Archibald
14. Steve Frew
15. Name the Scots gymnast who won bronze in the High Bar at the 2006 Commonwealth Games in Melbourne
16. Adam Cox
17. Elephant Polo
18. Donald Dinnie
19. Dougal Haston
20. At 51, she became the oldest British woman to conquer the peak
21. England
22. Sinead and John Kerr

Miscellaneous Sports: First Division 2

1. He is the haggis-hurling world record holder
2. Duncan Airlie James
3. Steve Lindsay
4. Steve Sinton
5. Bill Anderson MBE
6. 4
7. Captain Robert Barclay Allardice
8. Dr Hamish McInnes
9. Isabel Newstead (nee Barr)
10. Jenni Brien
11. Barry Collie
12. Weightlifting (Men's 94 kg Snatch)
13. Campbell Walsh
14. John White
15. He reached world No.1 in March 2004
16. He won 4 gold medals over 3 Games
17. Lee Beachill
18. Jonathon Power
19. 60
20. Inverurie

Picture Quiz

Old Firm / Hearts and Hibs

1. Maurice Edu and Marc Crosas
2. Dixie Deans
3. 2: Stilian Petrov scored Celtic's 3rd goal
4. Left to right: Derek Johnstone, Sandy Jardine, Alex McDonald and Peter McCloy
5. 2
6. Vladimir Romanov
7. Steven Pressley
8. Derek Riordan

North of the Tay / Scotland

1. Bobby Cox
2. Fabrizio Ravanelli
3. Eddie Thompson
4. Ivan Golac
5. Zander Diamond
6. 5: he achieved this in every season he was there
7. 2: the European Championships in 1996 and the World Cup in 1998
8. Berti Vogts

Other Sports

1. Roger Federer
2. Elena Baltacha
3. Matt Williams
4. Chris Paterson
5. John Leslie
6. Bill McLaren
7. 5
8. Carnoustie
9. Lloyd Saltman
10. Allan McNish
11. 3
12. Left to right: Graeme Dott, Drew Henry, Stephen Maguire, and Stephen Hendry
13. Rhona Martin
14. Sailing
15. Tony Hand
16. Liz McColgan